最新 觀光/飯店/餐飲 英語

Hotel and Restaurant English Made Easy

Forde Sakuoka 著

附錄音帶

前　　言

　　這本書是針對目前從事飯店及餐飲業人士，或是今後準備踏入這個業界的人士所編的基礎飯店業務及餐飲用的英語會話教材。

　　學習英語會話，也許要花費許多時間而且在學習過程中常會覺得很麻煩，有時也會有不知道從何處開始著手的難處。關於英語，因為大家在學校裡都經過了許多年的學習，在閱讀簡單的英語文章時，也都能理解大部分的內容。但是若要表達時，往往只在腦裡思考而不知該如何表現，而怯於開口，這也是初學者在學習過程中常碰到的情形。

　　此本書，是以東京ＹＭＣＡ國際飯店專門學校的教材為基礎，將日常業務中使用頻率較高；且表現上較簡潔的文句，以優先順序做了一個整理，只要將本書表現予以融會貫通，相信對於業務上簡單的應對及處理上，應該能夠駕輕就熟。

　　雖然是簡單的表現，但如果以有自信的方式表現出來的話，那麼你的進步將會令人大吃一驚。因此在這裡，請讀者將本書的基本表現先求熟練並培養自信心，接著再求進一步的精研。

　　最後在整理此書之時，得到東京ＹＭＣＡ國際飯店專門學校的遠矢主幹、教務部的諸位先進及ＰＬＡＺＡ出版社的柴山先生等的鼎力協助，特此致謝。

作者 Forde　Sakuoka

引　　　言

　　國內的觀光事業，經政府開放外國人落地簽証後，已有大幅度的成長。各大飯店無不爲了提昇服務的水準，而在硬體及軟體上下了相當的努力，因此近年來我國五星級飯店的水準也日益提高。

　　在諸多服務的項目中，軟體方面，即「人的服務」是客人在享受飯店的各種設施之餘，所最直接感受到飯店親切服務的一面，這時所仰賴的是我們將這一份服務的熱忱，用「語言」及「態度」來表現。而外語的表現能力，也是一個關鍵，訓練員工的專業語文能力，也是每一個國際飯店人力資源部訓練的重點之一。

　　坊間也有許多類似的書籍，但是細讀之下，還是以此書的編排較易使初學者了解各個場面的回答方式。此本書並附錄有許多飯店及餐飲常用單字，使從事餐飲、飯店業人員能夠即學即用，並運用於工作上，以達到學以致用。

　　在此很高興看到這本書的出版，希望讀者能自此書中吸收豐富的知識並學習基本的應對能力，使得全體餐飲業的服務及語言水平得以提昇。

台北晶華酒店　　人力資源部

協理　

引　　言

　　如果你喜歡與各國人交談及讓每一位客人肯定你的工作，那麼觀光旅館業會是你最佳的選擇！

　　為了提高顧客的滿意度以及持續的惠顧，觀光旅館從業人員不僅僅是需要有親切的笑容、專業的服務技能外，語言也是觀光旅館業人員所應具備的重要條件之一。因此，培養良好的語文會話能力，將會使你愉快地勝任這項服務工作。

　　至於如何培養良好的飯店及餐飲方面的會話能力？首先得要有一本好的工具書與錄音帶，加上反覆不斷的練習，培養自信並大聲的說出來，假以時日，你就能將各種表現駕輕就熟的表達。如果每一位服務人員，都能基於顧客的需要，提供適切的服務，定能使客人感到賓至如歸，而飯店的良好服務是冀於每一個成員的努力。

　　漢思有限公司有鑑於語言對觀光旅館從業人員的重要性，得到東京 PLAZA 出版社及 YMCA 國際飯店觀光學校的授權，編譯了「最新觀光飯店、餐飲英語」一書以饗讀者。相信如藉由基本會話語句及配合實際業務上的高頻率用語表現，同時再配合錄音帶學習的話，會引領讀者有效的提昇自己語文方面的能力。

台北圓山大飯店　教育訓練中心

副主任　王月碧

■ 著 者 簡 介

Forde　Sakuoka：
生於夏威夷歐湖島。畢業於布利坎揚格大學教育學部。
為東京ＹＭＣＡ國際飯店專門學校的專任講師，從事英
語教育 10 年以上。

> 增加您學習的效率及矯正發音
> 本書並附有錄音帶可加快您學習的速度

如果想使英語會話說得更加流暢，以加強聽力及學習正
確的發音，為最重要的步驟。本書附錄的「會話練習」
、「音調練習」、「置換練習」、「發音要訣」，都是
由美國籍的專業播音員所錄製而成。在學習時，可以一
邊聽一邊練習，保證您的聽力及會話能力必定大為提昇
並且進步神速。

＊因為尊重原著且原錄音者發音非常清楚悅耳，因此錄
　音帶在文中將地名、價格部分，予以保留，請留意。

錄音者：　Tom　Clark　，　Gerri　Sorrells
　　　　　1 － A　　Lesson　1 ~ Lesson 10
　　　　　1 － B　　Lesson 11 ~ Lesson 21

6

編 者 的 話

　　此本書原爲日本 PLAZA 出版社出版之「 Hotel and Restaurant English Made Easy 」，在日本爲長年暢銷書，讀者群不但包括飯店業的從業人員，也適宜各行各業的人閱讀。因爲內容包涵基本會話、打招呼問候語以及推薦事務的用法，同時也是一本在接待客人、出國觀光、旅遊時的一本多方位即學即用的入門書。

　　此本書也提供給各大飯店做爲員工教育訓練的指定教材，因此本公司同時也一併製作錄音帶以饗讀者。在台灣逐漸邁向國際化的今天，引領觀光飯店業的蓬勃發展；我們需要多方面相關的書籍，來提高我們的語言能力。

　　今後本公司也會在此學習系列中另外繼續推出「最新觀光飯店餐飲日語會話」，使學習外國語的瓶頸，經由有系統的整理，來加快大家的學習的腳步。在書末並附錄有飯店、餐飲的常用單字，方便讀者迅速查到所需的單字，以減少查單字所耗費的時間。同時也可豐富讀者的字彙能力。

　　最後也希望讀者以此書奠定紮實的基礎，迎接這國際化的時代。在此特別感謝晶華酒店人力資源部朱順風協理、鄭雯心主任和圓山大飯店人事訓練王耳碧小姐的協助；及參與本翻譯與編輯製作的同仁林麗文、林吟美、莊宜燕、施怡蓮等人，以及日本 PLAZA 出版社的柴山社長使得本書得以順利出版，在此一併申謝。

編者謹誌

「本書的構成及使用方法」

　　本書的構成是以基本的會話語句 PART I (第 1 章 -第 10 章),及在實際業務的執行時,使用頻率較高的語句及表現,整理於 PART II (第 11 章 -第 21 章),各章並區分下列的項目,如果先能理解每個項目的學習目的及特色後,再開始學習的話,相信一定能夠提昇學習的效果。此外,本書並附有錄音帶(另售),在此也推薦您一起配合學習。

《會話練習》　　　　　　此單元列出基本文型的對話實
　　　　　　　　　　　　例。讀者可以一邊練習;一邊
　　　　　　　　　　　　聯想對話的表現是使用在何種
　　　　　　　　　　　　場面上。

《常用高頻率會話》　　　將使用頻率較高的基本表現做
　　　　　　　　　　　　了整理並逐一列出;同時附錄
　　　　　　　　　　　　說明,使您一目瞭然,瞭解使
　　　　　　　　　　　　用的時機。
　　　　　　　　　　　　(錄音帶部份省略)

《音調練習》　　　　　　此單元整理相關的句型，配合錄
　　　　　　　　　　　　音帶一起學習，讓您的發音字正
　　　　　　　　　　　　腔圓並且能夠熟悉英語音調的發
　　　　　　　　　　　　音。

《置換練習》　　　　　　將基本的表現，依照各個場面做
　　　　　　　　　　　　會話的置換練習，加強句型的應
　　　　　　　　　　　　用，讓您習慣英語會話的表現方
　　　　　　　　　　　　法。

《發音要訣》　　　　　　針對不易發音的部分，說明發音的
　　　　　　　　　　　　方法。整理並列舉相關的單字，讓
　　　　　　　　　　　　您練習正確的發音。
　　　　　　　　　　　　(附錄於 PART I)

《英語會話要訣》　　　　告訴您學習英語的要訣及方法。
　　　　　　　　　　　　(附錄於 PART I)

《寫作實力養成練習》　　培養會話中英語作文的實力。
　　　　　　　　　　　　(附錄於 PART II)

目　　次

PART I

讓我們先熟記英語會話中的基本事項

Lesson 1 問 候 用 語

　　與他人見面時，禮貌上要先問候對方，這也是出社會最重要的一課。當然用中文表達誰都沒有問題，但是以英語來說時，有的人就會怯場。英語中的表現也有固定的慣用句，讓我們一起來練習。在發音時一定要清楚，那麼接下來的會話，也會較流暢。

May I help you?

《 **Dialogue Drill　1** 》　　*G*: Guest, *C*: Clerk
G:　Hi!
C:　Good morning, ma'am.　May I help you?
G:　Yes.　Where is the Coffee Shop?
C:　It's over there, ma'am.
G:　Oh, I see.　Thank you.
C:　Not at all.

《 **Dialogue Drill　2** 》　　*G*: Guest, *B*: Bellgirl
B:　Good afternoon, sir.　Welcome to the Plaza Hotel.
G:　Thank you.
B:　Are you checking in, sir?
G:　Yes.　Where is the Front Desk?
B:　I'll show you the way, sir.　This way, please.
G:　O.K.

需要我效勞嗎？

《會話練習 1》　　*G*: 客人，　*C*: 飯店櫃檯人員
　G:　請問……
　C:　早安，女士。需要我效勞嗎？
　G:　是的。請問咖啡廳在那裏？
　C:　在那邊。女士。
　G:　哦，我明白了。謝謝。
　C:　不客氣。

《會話練習 2》　　*G*: 客人，　*B*: 女行李員
　B:　午安，先生。歡迎光臨廣場大飯店。
　G:　謝謝。
　B:　先生，您要辦理住宿登記嗎？
　G:　是的。請問櫃檯在那裏？
　B:　先生，我來為您帶路。請往這邊。
　G:　好的。

《常用高頻率會話》

*Good morning , sir (ma'am).

英語常用此種問候用語。上午是使用 " Good morning"
，下午是 " Good afternoon" ，傍晚五點以後是用
" Good evening" 。

*~, sir (ma'am).

對男性客人是用 sir，女性客人是用 ma'am，在文章的
最後加上此一敬稱。但是請特別注意對女性客人是不能
使用 sir。年輕女性客人也是使用 ma'am。對於小孩子
可以不用加上任何敬稱。在使用敬稱時必須適當，用在
會話的最初、最後及重要的部分就可以了。不可像中文
中 "王先生(王 sir)" 在姓氏後面加上此敬稱。

*How are you this morning?

「今早好嗎？」
對於熟的客人，如果再加上此句，可以讓會話有個愉快
的開始。在美國此句問候語經常在迎接客人時所使用。

*May I help you?

直譯的意思是「需要我效勞嗎？」，在商務會話用法上，
語意有點接近「歡迎光臨」。在介紹事務，或是在對顧
客提供服務時，都可加上此句。

*Welcome to the~. 「歡迎到~」

在迎接客人時的標準會話語句，有時在餐廳中也常聽到，在正式的會話中，經常使用此句來表示歡迎之意，如果你還不熟悉的話，省略也無所謂。

*Hello!, Hi! (客人用語)

相當於「你好！」。「Hi！」是用在較不正式場合的打招呼用語，如同中文的「嗨！」，與客人應對時，儘量不要使用。

*I'm fine., Just fine., Pretty good.

"How are you~?" 的回答用句。「我很好（不錯）。」的意思，因為是慣用語，因此即使心情不太好，還是會使用（避免把壞心情帶給別人）。如果心情真的很不好，可以使用 Not bad. (馬馬虎虎) 等語句。

「有關天氣的表現語句」

*It's a beautiful day, isn't it?
　「今天天氣真好。」
　(a nice day, a pleasant day)
*It will probably rain tomorrow.
　「明天大概會下雨吧?」
　(be fair, be cloudy)
*It's hot today, isn't it ?
　「今天真熱啊。」
　(cold: 冷 , warm: 暖和)

17

《音調練習》　 (*是特別加重發音的部分)
1) Good morning. (↘)
2) Good afternoon. (↘)
3) Good evening. (↘)
4) How a*re you? (↘)
5) How are you? (↗ ：回答的時候)
6) How a*re you this morning? (↘)
7) How are yo*u today? (↘)
8) Fine, thank you.
9) I'm fine, thank you.
10) It's a beautiful day, isn't it? (↘)

《置換練習》
1) Good <u>morning, ma'am.</u>
　　　　afternoon, sir.
　　　　evening, ma'am.

2) How are you <u>this morning?</u>
　　　　　　　this afternoon?
　　　　　　　this evening?

3) It's <u>a beautiful day</u>, isn't it?
　　　a nice day,
　　　a pleasant day,

4) It's <u>hot</u> today, isn't it?
　　　cold
　　　warm
　　　muggy　(muggy: 酷熱，悶熱)

18

《發音要訣》〔 p 〕與〔 b 〕的發音

　　將上下嘴唇，輕輕的合上，再用力吹氣發出〔 p 〕
與〔 b 〕的音。但是不可以發得太重。

〔發音練習〕

pack	〔 p æ k 〕	back	〔 b æ k 〕
pick	〔 ` p ɪ k 〕	big	〔 b ɪ g 〕
push	〔 p ʊ ʃ 〕	better	〔 ` b ɛ t ɚ 〕
pen	〔 p ɛ n 〕	boy	〔 b ɔ ɪ 〕
post	〔 p o s t 〕	book	〔 b ʊ k 〕

《英文會話要訣》　〔首先讓我們來做發音練習！〕

　　要說一口流利的英語，一定要經常開口練習。在一
般的會話上所使用的單字及句型，都不會太難，如能反
覆的練習並掌握英語的音調和發音，就比較有自信用英
語表達與應對。不管文法觀念有多麼正確，如果發音不
對，有時還是容易造成誤解，甚至令對方不明瞭你要表
達的意思。

　　在 Part I 的發音練習上，特別將較難的發音及容易
發錯的音，列出來加以解說。在發音時，也要注意重音
節的位置。此外在做對話練習時，句子的段落及語尾，
要特別發清楚。

Lesson 2　回答

　　會話是雙方面的對話，而不是單行道。特別是當對方為客人時，要注意回答必須明確及具體。回答的表現，依照狀況可分為幾種方式。因此先視情況，將回答的方式熟記即可臨機應變。在回答時，一定要明確的表示出 YES 及 NO。不知所云的微笑，或是啞口無言都會令客人感到不安。

Certainly, ma'am.

《 **Dialogue Drill　1** 》　　*G*: Guest, *D*: Doorman

D:　Good morning, ma'am.

G:　Good morning.　Could you call a taxi for me, please?

D:　Certainly, ma'am.　Just a moment, please...
　　Here's your taxi.

G:　Thank you.

D:　You're welcome, ma'am.

《 **Dialogue Drill　2** 》　　*G*: Guest, *W*: Waitress

W:　Which would you prefer, tea or coffee?

G:　Coffee, please.

W:　Certainly, sir.　Will there be anything else?

G:　No, that's all thanks.

W:　Thank you.　I'll bring your coffee immediately, sir.

好的，女士。

《會話練習 1》　　*G*: 客人，　*D*: 門僮

　　D:　早安，女士。

　　G:　早安。麻煩請幫我叫一輛計程車。

　　D:　好的，女士。請稍待...
　　　　　您的計程車來了。

　　G:　謝謝。

　　D:　不客氣。

《會話練習 2》　　*G*: 客人，*W*: 女服務生

　　W:　請問您要點咖啡還是紅茶？

　　G:　請給我咖啡。

　　W:　好的，先生。請問還要點其他的嗎？

　　G:　不，就點這些。謝謝。

　　W:　謝謝您。我會馬上為您送咖啡來。

《常用高頻率會話》
*Certainly, sir (ma'am).
回答時使用。相當於「當然（遵命）」的意思。
此外也有類似的「 I see, ma'am., Very well, sir., Yes, ma'am.」等的表現。
O.K., Yeah 等因爲是屬於俚語，因此不可以對客人使用。

*Just a moment, please.
「請稍等...」的意思。特別是在自己無法回答，或是在聽不懂對方所表達的意思時使用，同時再轉請其他負責的人來處理。

*Thank you for waiting, ma'am (sir).
「讓您久等了。」的意思。如果讓對方等待很久而感到抱歉時，可使用 " I'm sorry to have kept you waiting."。在餐廳會話中，除非是眞的讓對方等很久，不然一般不說也無妨。

*Here it is.
將物品交給對方時的慣用語，意思是「請」。相同的類語有 Here you are., Here is your~。在此時不能加上 " Please "，如果加上 " Please "，是表示拜託的意思。

*You're welcome, ma'am (sir).

「不客氣。」，在對方說 Thank you 時的回答。

相同的類語有 " Not at all." , " Don't mention it ."

*Thank you, ma'am (sir).

「謝謝您。」

任何人都能夠朗朗上口的一句話，可用在餐廳的應對或是接受客人點菜、付帳時。英美人士，常會加上此句以表示客氣。你也可以多多使用此句。此句比使用 Certainly, sir. 或是 Yes, sir." 的表現更得體，且還帶有一份感謝之情。

*Have a nice day.

「預祝您今天心情愉快。」，在 day 之外也可以置換成 evening , weekend , holiday , vacation 等。

*Please enjoy your~.

在中文中，較無此類似的表現，可解釋成「請慢用」、「請享用」的意思。使用的場合是在客人離開時，或是提供餐點時，可在~之後加上 lunch 或是 dinner 。如果是住宿的客人，則可在~之後加上 stay 。

《音調練習》
1) Certainly, sir.
2) Just a moment, please.
3) Thank you for waiting, ma'am.
4) Here is your taxi.
5) Thank you,sir.
6) Thank yöu, ma'am. (當對方說 Thank you 時的回答)
7) Have a nice day.
8) Please enjoy your stay.
9) You're welcome.
10) Not at all.

《置換練習》
1) Here it is.
       you are.
       is your key.

2) Have a nice day.
          evening.
          time.

3) Please enjoy your stay.
             breakfast.
             dinner.

4) I'll bring your coffee immediately, ma'am.
             baggage
             bill

《發音要訣》〔f〕與〔v〕的發音

發音的方式是以上面的牙齒，輕輕的壓在下唇，將積於口中的氣，以較強烈的方式發出〔f〕與〔v〕的音。在發此音時，可以感覺到下唇有彈向外側的感覺。若壓太緊的話，會造成下唇不會動，而發不出音來。如果在單字末尾發此音時，會將下唇壓住後再發此音。

〔發音練習〕

family	〔ˋfæməlɪ〕	value	〔ˋvælju〕
fee	〔fi〕	view	〔ˋvju〕
food	〔fud〕	very	〔ˋvɛrɪ〕
photo	〔ˋfoto〕	voice	〔vɔɪs〕
fence	〔fɛns〕	vivid	〔ˋvɪvɪd〕

《英語會話要訣》

在英語中因為有重音節的關係，所以在文章及單字的發音上就會有強弱的分別。每一個單字都有重音節，因此重音發不正確時，會變成不同的意思，或是造成對方聽不懂的窘境。

同時，能夠注意句子中的重要詞句或是關鍵語的音調，那麼就很容易聽懂對方在說些什麼，如此一來將可很容易的了解會話中的重點。

Lesson 3　拒　絕；道　歉

　　每一國家的語言都是一樣，在會話中較難表現的語句是如何拒絕對方。特別是當對方是客人的時候，如果表現上未能婉轉的拒絕，也許會得罪客人，喪失下次的交易機會。但是如果太過於禮貌，也會造成失禮。因此，在說明上要明確，避免含糊不清，造成誤會。

I'm very sorry, sir....

《 **Dialogue Drill** 》　　*G*: Guest, *C*: Clerk

C:　Good morning, Plaza Hotel.　May I help you?

G:　Yes, please.　I'd like to make a reservation for next Monday.

C:　I'm sorry, sir, but we are all booked for the next week.

G:　Nothing at all?

C:　No, sir.　This is the busiest season.　I'm very sorry, sir. But could you call us again later on this week?　We may have a cancellation, sir.

G:　Okay, I'll do that.　Thanks.

C:　You're welcome, sir.

很抱歉，先生‧‧‧‧‧

《會話練習》　　G: 客人，　C: 飯店櫃檯人員

C: 早安，<u>廣場</u>大飯店。需要我效勞嗎？

G: 是的，我想預約下星期一。

C: 很抱歉，先生，下星期全客滿了。

G: 都沒有空的房間嗎？

C: 是的。因爲現在是旺季。非常抱歉，先生。請您下星期一再打電話來詢問好嗎？也許會有人取消訂房。

G: 好的，我會再打來。謝謝。

C: 不客氣。先生。

《常用高頻率會話》

在拒絕對方時，一定要先確認對方說話的內容，同時要站在對方的立場來做回答。如需表示歉意時，可以轉給職位較高的人員，由有經驗的人來處理。

*I'm afraid~.

相當於「很對不起，恐怕……」的意思。如果沒有辦法遵照客人的意思時，與其說 No,~.還不如使用此句，會讓對方感覺較親切。

*I'm sorry~.

「很對不起….，但….」的意思。想拒絕對方時，可以使用此句。其中 Sorry 的意思是當你覺得「很抱歉，真可惜」時使用。此外覺得「很令人惋惜」也可使用 I'm sorry.。

- I'm sorry to hear that.
  「那真是令人惋惜的消息。」
- I'm sorry I couldn't help you.
  「很抱歉不能幫上忙。」

*Excuse me.

這句話使用的範圍很廣。在穿越人群之前或是退席時使用。意思上如同「對不起；失禮了」。此外，在呼喚對方時，也會使用此句話作為開頭語。

*I must apologize for~.

「對….感到抱歉」，這是表示對對方感到歉意的表現。通常是由該負責的人，來做道歉的表示。

〔**關於 Yes 和 No 的表現**〕

　　在英語的表現方法中，對於 YES 與 NO 的表現要特別注意，一般而言肯定的疑問句型並不會有太大的問題，但是在否定的疑問句型中，回答時不可以肯定句來表示。此外在附加疑問句（例：~, isn't it ?）時也容易搞錯。請參考下面的例文，徹底的了解正確的表現方法。(簡單的說，如果回答是肯定的，那就用 YES。如果回答是否定的，那就用 NO。前後文要統一。)

*Is the bar open now?
　「酒吧現在有營業嗎？」
　　Yes, it is.　「是，有的。」
*The bar isn't open, is it?
　「酒吧現在沒有營業，是嗎？」
　　Yes, it is.　「不，它已經營業了。」
*Isn't the bar open now?
　「酒吧現在沒有營業吧？」
　　Yes, it is.　「不，已經有營業了。」
*Is the barber shop open now?
　「理髮店現在有營業嗎？」
　　No, it isn't.　「不，沒開。」
*The barber shop isn't open, is it?
　「理髮店現在沒有營業，是嗎？」
　　No, it isn't.　「對，它沒有營業。」
*Isn't the barber shop open now?
　「理髮店現在沒有營業吧？」
　　No, it isn't.　「是的，它沒有。」

1）I'm sorry, but we have no rooms available.
2）We're all booked until the end of the month.
3）We're all booked for the next week.
4）We may have a cancellation.
5）Excuse me for a moment.
6）Will you excuse me for a second?
7）I'm afraid we don't.
8）I'm sorry I couldn't help you.

《置換練習》

1）I'm sorry, but they are all sold out.
　　　　　　　　 it's not in season now.
　　　　　　　　 we don't accept personal checks.
　　　　　　　　 we are not allowed to do that.

2）I'm afraid we don't.
　　　　　　 we can't.
　　　　　　 we don't have any singles available.
　　　　　　 we have no tables open at the moment.

3）I must apologize for the mistake.
　　　　　　　　　　 for the mix-up.
　　　　　　　　　　 for the inconvenience.

《發音要訣》〔 t 〕, 〔 k 〕, 〔 d 〕的發音
　　這些音如果是在單字的語尾時，嘴唇會輕輕的張開，會稍微以出力的方式發出強音。〔 d 〕是如同在喉嚨發出有反響的聲音，如果練習一下，很容易發得出來。

〔發音練習〕

cut	〔 k ʌ t 〕	did	〔 d ɪ d 〕
but	〔 b ʌ t 〕	red	〔 r ɛ d 〕
sit	〔 s ɪ t 〕	kid	〔 k ɪ d 〕
kick	〔 k ɪ k 〕		
cook	〔 k ʊ k 〕		
pick	〔 p ɪ k 〕		

《英文會話要訣》〔對於經常使用的表現，就把它背起來〕
　　常看到許多人在與外國人交談時，只會使用單字來回答，而無法表達完整的句型。當然如果能夠說一口流暢的英語，是多麼令人羨慕的一件事。每個人都會想達到那個境界，而最快的方法就是把慣用語句背起來。
　　如能背誦文章的話，不但可以把英語本身的音調學起來，同時要用到之時，也可馬上脫口而出。如果把本書中 Part I 中出現的高頻率會話先記起來，那麼基本的日常生活會話也應該足以應付。

Lesson 4 聽 不 懂 對 方 在 說 些 什 麼 ?

　　對於初學者而言，當對方向你開口說英語時，往往會令人感到害怕。但是必須要了解客人是因爲有事才會找你，如果沒辦法聽懂或是無法理解時，請對方再說一遍，是不會造成失禮的。以客人本身而言，如果不是以英語爲母語的人或是腔調等的關係，都會使人較難於理解，若眞的聽不懂時，可以早一點請負責的人來幫忙。

I beg your pardon?

《 **Dialogue Drill** 》　　*V*: Visitor, *C*: Clerk

V: Excuse me.　What room are Mr. and Mrs. Jones in?

C: I beg your pardon?

V: I'd like to know Mr. and Mrs. Jones's room number.

C: Are they with a tour, sir?

V: Yes, they are.　The American Express Tour.

C: Thank you, sir.　Just a moment, please....
　　Yes, Mr. and Mrs. Jones are in room six ten, sir.

V: Thank you.

C: You're welcome, sir.

能否再重述一遍？

《會話練習》　　V: 客人，　C: 飯店櫃檯人員
V: 請問瓊斯夫婦住在幾號房？
C: 對不起，請再說一次？
V: 我想知道瓊斯夫婦住在幾號房？
C: 先生，請問他們是跟隨旅行團嗎？
V: 是的。美國運通旅行團。
C: 謝謝，請稍等。
　　有了，先生，瓊斯夫婦是住在 610 號房間。
V: 謝謝。
C: 不客氣。

《常用高頻率會話》
*Pardon me., I beg your pardon.
　「請再說一遍好嗎？」
　在發音時要將語尾提高。與 Excuse me. 的意思相近。

*Could you repeat that, please?
　「請再重述一遍好嗎？」

*Could you speak more slowly, please?
　Would you mind speaking more slowly?
　「請說慢一點好嗎？」

*I'm afraid I don't understand.
　「對不起，我不太明白」
　特別是在會話中感覺語意複雜時，或是關鍵的語句沒
　辦法了解時，可以使用這句話。這時對方應該會用其
　他方式來表現。 I'm afraid 也可以用 Excuse me, but~.
　這句話來替換。

*Just a moment, please.　I'll get (call) the manager.
　「請稍等一下，我會請負責的經理來」
　如果沒有辦法了解會話的內容，或是太複雜時，要趁
　早請負責的人出面處理。如果負責的人不在現場，可
　以用 call 來代替 get 。此外也可說成 Let me get the
　manager. 。

〔姓名等的確認〕

*Excuse me.　How do you spell your name?
「對不起，請問如何拼您的名字？」
在確認是否有預約時，客人的名字的正確拼音一定要先
作確認。這是因爲客人姓名的固有名詞、拼音及讀音，
常有獨特的唸法。此外，W 的讀音，常常與 double 混
淆，如果還是聽不懂時，可以下列例句來表示。

・Could you write down your name, please?
　「請寫下您的大名？」

同時，在字跡潦草而無法辨認的時候
・Could you write it in print?
　「麻煩請用正楷書寫」

*Excuse me.　How do you pronounce your name?
「很抱歉，您的大名怎麼唸？」

〔馬上回答是一種禮貌〕
　　在被詢問的時候，必須馬上做回答。如果沈默不
語，對方會誤認爲他所說的話，你可能聽不懂，而無
法放心。如果被客人詢問，而需要一些時間思索時，
可以使用下列的表現方法。

・Let me see.　(讓我想一下....)
・Well.　　　　(那麼....)

35

《音調練習》
1) Excuse me. (↘ .語調下降是抱歉的意思)
2) Excuse me. (↗ .請問您說什麼？)
3) I beg your pardon? (↗)
4) Could you repeat that, please?
5) I'm afraid I don't understand.
6) Just a moment, please.　I'll get the manager.
7) Let me get the manager.　Just a moment, please.
8) Would you mind repeating what you said?
9) Is that with a double "T"?
10) Let me see......

《置換練習》

1) How do you spell your name?
　　　　　　　　your first name? (given)
　　　　　　　　your last name? (family)
　　　　　　　　it? (that, street, city, etc)

2) I'm afraid I don't understand.
　　　　　　I don't understand what you said.
　　　　　　I didn't quite catch what you said.

3) Would you mind repeating what you said?
　　　　　　　　repeating your question?
　　　　　　　　repeating the name again?
　　　　　　　　speaking more slowly?

《發音要訣》〔ʤ〕，〔tʃ〕的發音
　將嘴唇彎成圓形，發出〔ʤ〕，〔tʃ〕　發此音並不
　難。

〔發音練習〕
judge	〔ʤ ʌ ʤ〕	chat	〔tʃ æ t〕
brige	〔b r ɪ ʤ〕	chip	〔tʃ ɪ p〕
page	〔p e ʤ〕	chew	〔tʃ u〕
joke	〔ʤ o k〕	chest	〔tʃ ɛ s t〕

《英語會話要訣》　〔若不開口說，是不會進步的〕
　　　　對英語會話還沒有自信的時候，大部分的人總是羞
　於開口。但是必須牢記的是，不論是任何語言，如要說
　得流利且很有自信，惟有不斷的反覆練習。初學者剛開
　始時不要把目標訂得太高，以為一開口就可以講得流利
　，要注意把自己想要說的句子，條理分明的分成幾句，
　然後如積木一般一塊塊的疊起來，這樣才容易使對方理
　解你要說些什麼。要記得不要被對方說話的速度所影響
　；慢慢的說、並且說清楚是很重要的學習步驟。

Lesson 5　拜託客人

在會話中最常出現的狀況是詢問對方的意見，或是拜託、要求對方。特別是像飯店類的服務業，都是基於客人的希望而提供服務，因此類似此種表現，使用頻率也較高。

Could you fill out the form, please?

《 **Dialogue Drill** 》　　*G*: Guest, *C*: Clerk

C: Good evening, sir.　May I help you?

G: Yes.　I made a reservation here for a room.

C: May I have your name, sir?

G: Jones. Bill Jones.

C: Thank you, sir.　Just a moment, please....
Yes, Mr. Jones.　Could you fill out this form, please?

G: Sure...Here you are.

C: Thank you, sir.　Your room is 233 on the second floor.
Here's your key.　The bellman will take your bags and show you to your room.

G: Thank you.

C: You're welcome, sir.　Please enjoy your stay with us.

麻煩您填寫這張表格好嗎？

《會話練習》　　*G*: 客人，　*C*: 飯店櫃檯人員

C: 晚安，先生。需要我效勞嗎？

G: 是的，我預約了房間。

C: 先生，請問您的大名？

G: 瓊斯。比爾・瓊斯。

C: 謝謝，請您稍待.....有了。
　　瓊斯先生，麻煩您填寫這張表格好嗎？

G: 沒問題....填寫好了。

C: 謝謝，您的房間在 2 樓 233 號房。
　　這是您的鑰匙。服務生會幫您提行李並為您帶
　　路。

G: 謝謝。

C: 別客氣。先生，願您住的愉快。

《常用高頻率會話》

　　在一般的會話中，詢問對方或是拜託對方時，常使用一般的詢問句或是命令形，如果要說得禮貌一點可以加上 May I ~? 或是 Could you ~? 等表現。

　　Will you ~? 或是 Can you ~? 這些表現雖然在日常會話中也常被使用，但是由於表現上會令人覺得有些命令的味道，因此對客人還是不要使用較妥當。

*May I have (ask) your name, please?

「能否請教您的大名？」

May I ~?是請問對方能否為我們做什麼，因此在表示自己的想法時，可以使用。此外，如在問句前加上 May I ask 會讓對方感覺較有禮貌。

- May I have your address?
    「請問您的住址？」
    (Where do you live?)
    (What is your address?)
- May I have your telephone number?
    「請問您的電話號碼？」
    (What is your telephone number?)
- May I ask what his name is again?
    「能否再請教一下他的大名？」
    (What is his name again?)
- May I have the name of the tour again?
    「能否再請教一下旅行團的名稱？」
- May I ask what time will be convenient for you, sir?
    「能否請問您什麼時間比較方便呢？」

- May I ask what time we may be expecting you?

  「能否請問您預定幾點到達？」
- May I see your passport, sir?

  「先生，能否讓我看一下您的護照？」
- May I reconfirm the information, ma'am?

  「女士，我能再確認這份資訊嗎？」
- May I ask where you can be reached?

  「請問在那裏能連絡到您？」

*Could you sign the bill, please?

「麻煩您在帳單上簽名？」

拜託對方時的禮貌表現：Could you ~? 在日常會話上
是使用問句或是命令形，也可在句尾加上 Please。

- Could you hold the line, please?

  「請您稍待(電話)。」

  (Hold the line, please?)
- Could you fill out the form, please?

  「麻煩您填寫這張表？」

  (Fill out the form, please?)
- Could you tell me where the station is?

  「請告訴我車站在那裏？」

  (Where is the station?)
- Could you sign here, please?

  「請在這裏簽名好嗎？」
- Could you wait a little longer, please?

  「請您稍待片刻好嗎？」

《音調練習》
1) May I ask what his name is again?
2) May I have the name of the tour again?
3) May I ask what time will be convenient for you, sir?
4) May I ask where you can be reached?
5) Could you tell me where the station is?
6) Could you sign here, please?
7) Could you wait a little longer, please?
8) Could you repeat the order, please?

《置換練習》
1) May I ask your name, sir?
       have your name, please?
       have your initials, please?
       have your address, please?
       have your telephone number, please?
       see your passport, please?

2) Could you fill out the form, please?
       hold the line, please?
       contact the Front Desk, please?
       let us know as soon as possible?
       repeat that, please?
       speak more slowly, please?

《發音要訣》 she 的〔ʃ〕和 see 的〔s〕

　　〔ʃ〕的發音嘴形像在發「噓」時的形狀，而〔s〕的發音像「嘶」，發音嘴形是唇部呈橫狀，讓小酒渦呈現出來，千萬不可發成「西」的音。

〔發音練習〕

shut	〔ʃʌt〕	sand	〔sænd〕
ship	〔ʃɪp〕	sink	〔sɪŋk〕
should	〔ʃud〕	sailor	〔`selɚ〕
shell	〔ʃɛl〕	salt	〔sɔlt〕
shoulder	〔ʃoldɚ〕	sleep	〔slip〕

《英文會話要訣》 〔一邊使用單字一邊記下來〕

　　在學生時代，常常為了記單字，總是在身上帶著單字本或是卡片，而感到非常吃力。但是要使英語會話進步，背誦單字卻是很重要的步驟。日常會話不像教科書一般，會先列出單字及其範圍。因此最好的方法是經常把辭典放在身邊，如果忘記單字時，就馬上查；同時只要是認識的單字，就嘗試著去用它。常常這樣練習的話，可逐漸了解單字的各種涵義及其使用的時機，而這也是一種具體且能快速進步的方法。此外，在查字典時，也要開口多唸幾遍，這是因為單字詞類的不同，發音也會有所不同的。

Lesson 6 確認客人的意見，推薦事物

能夠針對客人的需要提供適切的服務，對飯店而言是非常重要的一件事。因此能夠正確的了解顧客的意向是非常重要的。在使用語句時，比 Do you want ~? 講得更客氣的用法是 Would you ~? 。此外，如果要讓客人採納自己意見時，可以使用 Shall I ~?的句型。

How would you like your steak?

《 **Dialogue Drill** 》　　*G*: Guest, *W*: Waitress

W: May I take your order, sir?

G: Yes.　We'll have this "Beef Steak Special".

W: Certainly, sir.　You may have a choice of vegetables: buttered spinach, french fries, green peas or mashed potatoes.

G: I'll have the buttered spinach and my wife will have the french fries.

W: Yes, sir.　How would you like your steak?

G: Medium for my wife and rare for me.

W: Yes, sir.　Would you like to have a cocktail before your meal?

G: Wine cooler for my wife and a bottle of beer for me.

W: Fine, sir.　Thank you.

請問牛排要幾分熟？

《會話練習》　　*G*: 客人，　*W*: 女服務生

W: 先生，請問您要點菜了嗎？

G: 是的，我們要點"牛排特餐"。

W: 好的，先生。
青菜有奶油炒菠菜、法式薯條、青豌豆
或是馬鈴薯泥可供選擇。

G: 我點奶油炒菠菜，我太太要法式薯條。

W: 好的，先生。
請問牛排要幾分熟？

G: 我太太要五分熟；我要三分熟。

W: 是的，先生。
是否要點些雞尾酒？

G: 請給我太太冰葡萄酒；給我來瓶啤酒。

W: 好的，謝謝您，先生。

《常用高頻率會話》

*Would you like a single or a twin?

「你要單人房或是雙人房？」在此使用 Would you ~? 來代替 Do you want ~? 會顯得更有禮貌。如果加上疑問詞時，會有下列的用法。

- What would you like to drink?
  「請問要喝點兒什麼？」
- When would you like to have your coffee served?
  「請問您咖啡要在什麼時候飲用？」
- Where would you like to sit?
  「請問您要坐那裏？」
- Who would you like to speak to?
  「請問您要和誰談話？」
- Which would you like (prefer), tea or coffee?
  「您要咖啡還是紅茶？」
- How would you like your steak?
  「請問牛排要幾分熟？」
- How much would you like to spend?
  「您的預算是多少？」
- How many nights would you like to extend?
  「您打算延長幾晚？」
- How long will you be staying with us?
  「您預定住多久？」

*Would you mind~ing
「您是否可以....」
推薦對方採納自己的意見時，可以使用此句，如：
- Would you mind opening the window?

*Shall I call the manager?
「我是否應該請負責的人過來？」
這是觀察客人的希望或是給與客人適當的意見時所使
用。與 Would you mind ~ing 的用法相同。

*Would you care for~
「~您覺得如何？」
請對方選擇時，可使用此句。
- Would you care for some more tea?

*How about~？
「~如何？」
比 Would you care for ~? 要來得通俗些，在日常會
中，也有使用 Why don't you ~? 這樣的說法。
- How about another cup of coffee?

*I advise you to take~.
I recommend that you take~.
I suggest that you take~.
I think you should take~.
「讓我推薦您....」

《音調練習》
1) Which brand would you like to have?
2) Would you care for tea (↗) or coffee? (↘)
3) Will there be anything else, sir?
4) Would you like your coffee with or after your meal?
5) Which dressing would you prefer? (↘)
6) I highly recommend it (the~).
7) You may have a choice of beans, potatoes or spinach.
8) Red wine goes well with your steak.

《置換練習》
1) Would you like to have a beer?
              to take a taxi?
              to visit the National Palace Museum?

2) Would you mind sharing a table?
               having a single room?
               waiting?

3) Shall I call the police?
          call a taxi?
          draw you a map?

4) Would you care for any wine?
                a cocktail?
                some ice cream?
                soup?

《發音要訣》〔m〕，〔n〕，〔ŋ〕的發音

發音時就如同聲音從鼻子出來。〔m〕與〔n〕是輕輕的把嘴唇合上，發出如「嘸」「嗯」的音。如果是單字字尾，在發此音時，是可以將氣一邊發出去，一邊將聲音停於口中。而〔ŋ〕是輕輕的將嘴唇打開發出此音。

〔發音練習〕

march	〔mɑrtʃ〕	noon	〔nun〕
miller	〔`mɪlɚ〕	tune	〔tjun〕
melody	〔`mɛlədɪ〕	morning	〔`mɔrnɪŋ〕
ma'am	〔mɑm〕	teaching	〔`titʃɪŋ〕
ham	〔hæm〕	speaking	〔`spikɪŋ〕
now	〔naʊ〕	eating	〔itɪŋ〕
note	〔not〕	going	〔`goɪŋ〕

《英文會話要訣》

會話的能力與聽力是相輔相成的，如果聽力好的話，那麼你的會話能力也會提高。而最有效的學習方法就是看外國電影。你可以隨著畫面與對話的表現來訓練自己的聽力，同時可以了解表現方法與使用的時機及相關的狀況。

Lesson 7 數 字 的 表 現

在日常會話中，數字的表現也常出現。在說明時間、金額、電話號碼、住址、場所、容積及容量時，一定會使用到數字，同時也要注意數字有各種特別的唸法，在讀時及表現上一定要正確，不要造成客人的誤解。

Your room is #2314.

《 **Dialogue Drill** 》　　*G*: Guest,*C*: Clerk

C:　Good evening, sir.　May I help you?

G:　Yes.　I'd like to have a room.

C:　What type of room would you like to have?

G:　A single with bath.

C:　I see, sir.　How long will you be staying?

G:　For three days, until next Monday.

C:　Fine, sir.　Let me check and see what we have.　Just a moment, please....
I'm sorry to have kept you waiting, sir.　We have a single with bath until next Monday.

G:　How much is it?

C:　It's NT$ 3,500 a night, plus a 10% tax and service charge.

G:　That'll be fine.

您的房間在 2314 號房。

《會話練習》　　G: 客人，　C: 飯店櫃檯人員

C: 晚安，先生。需要我效勞嗎？

G: 是的，我想訂一間房間。

C: 您想訂那一種房間呢？

G: 附浴室的單人房。

C: 好的，先生。您打算住幾天？

G: 住到下星期一，共三天。

C: 好，先生。請稍待一下，我查查看有沒有適合您的房間。很抱歉，讓您久等了。
我們有一間附有浴室的單人房，您可住到星期一。

G: 要多少錢？

C: 住一晚要台幣 3,500 元，外加 10%的營業稅和服務費。

G: 那可以。

《常用高頻率會話》

*NT$138,765

以英語表示數字時，讀法上是以三位為單位來唸。

1,000	thousand	（千）
1,000,000	million	（百萬）
1,000,000,000	billion	（十億）

如例文是唸成 One hundred thirty-eight thousand seven hundred and sixty-five NT Dollars.

*I'm leaving on the 10th.

「我 10 號離開」

日期用序數表示。

October 12th 1996　10-12-96	（美語）
the 12th of October 1996　12-10-96	（英語）

請不要將 date (日期)與 day (星期)的表示用法搞混。

Today is Thursday.　It's Thursday.

Today is the twenty-second.

Today is Thursday, the twenty-second.

表示時間或期間時可使用 on, for, until, since

on Sunday	（在星期日）
for 10 days	（10 天）
by Wednesday	（在星期三之前。表示期限）
until Saturday	（直到星期六。表示持續）
since last week	（從上星期）

*He was born in 1955. (nineteen fifty-five)

年號是以 2 位數分開來唸，電話號碼也是一樣。

*The Restaurant is on the 3rd floor.

樓層用序數來表示。

*It's 10:30. (ten thirty)

表示時間時,使用 past, to, quarter 等表現,但也可以直接以時、分的順序來唸。

What time is it? (現在幾點?)與 Do you have the time?的意思相同,也可使用這句話,請一起記下來。

It's ten o'clock. (10:00)　　(10 點整)

It's ten of five. (10:05)　　It's five past ten. (10 點過 5 分)

It's ten fifteen. (10:15)　　It's a quarter past ten.
　　　　　　　　　　　　　　(10 點過 1 刻)

It's ten thirty. (10:30)　　It's half past ten. (10 點半)

It's ten thirty-seven. (10:37) It's twenty-three minutes to eleven.
　　　　　　　　　　　　　　(差 23 分到 11 點)

It's ten forty-five. (10:45)　It's a quarter to eleven.
　　　　　　　　　　　　　　(差 1 刻到 11 點)

It's twelve noon (midnight). (午夜)

〔**關於日期等的讀法**〕

tonight	(今晚)
the day before yesterday	(前天)
the night before last	(前天夜晚)
the day after tomorrow	(後天)
the week after next	(下下週)
every other day	(隔天)
every three days	(每三天一次)
leap year	(閏年)
the second Sunday of every month	(每個月第二個星期天)

《音調練習》
1) Your room is #503. (five oh three)
2) Your room is #2314. (twenty-three, fourteen)
3) Your room is #1112. (eleven, twelve)
4) Your room is on the 11th floor.
5) NT$1,500(one thousand five hundred NT Dollars)
6) Breakfast is served from 7:30.(不用加 a.m.)
7) The concert begins at 7:30.(不用加 p.m.)
8) He will arrive at 7:30 p.m. tomorrow.
9) I met him the day before yesterday.
10) I'm on duty every other day.

《置換練習》
1) I'm going to leave on September 13th.
              stay for 7 days.
              wait until next Monday.

2) It's 10:30.   (ten thirty)
        9:43.   (nine forty-three)
        5:05.   (five oh five)
        2:26.   (two twenty-six)

3) It's on the 3rd floor.
              15th floor.
              22nd floor.

《發音要訣》〔l〕和〔r〕的發音

這兩個音較難發，在拼單字時請特注意單字的拼法來區別〔l〕和〔r〕的發音。請仔細的分辨。

〔發音練習〕

people	〔 ˋpipl〕	racket	〔 ˋrækɪt〕
apple	〔 ˋæpl〕	rain	〔ren〕
look	〔luk〕	teacher	〔 ˋtitʃɚ〕
listen	〔 ˋlɪsn̩〕	doctor	〔 ˋdɑktɚ〕
lucky	〔 ˋlʌkɪ〕	remember	〔rɪˋmɛmbɚ〕

《英文會話要訣》

英語的構成與國語不同，因此在造句時要依照英文的文法。如果不知道這個單字怎麼說，這時要發揮自己的想像力，用其他的字來置換。如果能夠說得簡單明瞭，對方會比較容易理解。

此外，讀文章及做聽力練習時，若遇到不懂的單字時，要以單字的前後關係來聯想這個字的意思。之後，再用字典來做確認的工作，這也是一種很好的學習方法。

Lesson 8 電 話 會 話

電話會話要比一般會話來的困難的原因是因爲在電話中看不到對方的表情，也沒有辦法以手勢確定對方的反應。因此，爲了避免造成誤會，應使用簡潔而明瞭的語句，同時要說得慢一點，幫助對方理解。

Go ahead, please.

《 **Dialogue Drill** 》 *G*: Guest, *O*: Operator

O: This is the Plaza Hotel.　May I help you?

G: May I have extension three oh eight?

O: Three zero eight?

G: Yes. please.

O: Thank you, sir.　Just a moment, please.
　　I'm sorry, sir.　The line is busy now.

G: Will you please keep on trying?

O: Yes, sir...
　　You're connected now.　Go ahead, please.

G: Thank you.

O: You're welcome, sir.

請通話

《會話練習》　　*G*: 客人，　*O*: 接線生
- *O*:　廣場大飯店，您好。
- *G*:　幫我接內線 308。
- *O*:　是 308 嗎？
- *G*:　是的。麻煩您。
- *O*:　謝謝，請您稍待。
　　　先生，抱歉，電話正忙線中。
- *G*:　請再幫我轉接看看好嗎？
- *O*:　好的，先生...
　　　接通了，請說。
- *G*:　謝謝。
- *O*:　先生，不客氣。

《常用高頻率會話》
*Speaking., Yes, it's me., Yes, it is.
　　對方來電話時的回答用語，如果對方說「是(王先生)
　　嗎？」以此句來回答的意思是「是的，我就是。」。
　　Yes, It is. 是用在對公司或是商店時，而 Yes, it's me.
　　是用在個人， Speaking. 是兩種情況均可使用。

*Is this the~?
　　打電話到對方公司時，「是~嗎？」的意思。在美語
　　是使用 Is this ~?，英語則是 Is that ~?

*May I speak to Mr.~?
　　I'd like to speak to ~.
　　Can I speak with ~?
　　Could you put me through to ~?
　　「幫我接~先生」，「~先生/小姐在嗎？」
　　請對方轉接給想要連絡的人。

*I'll connect you with the ~.
　　「轉接給~」

*Go ahead, please.
　　「請說。」

*The line is busy.
　　「電話忙線中。」

*Could you hold the line, please?
　「請稍待。」
　(比 Hold on, please. 的用法更有禮貌)

*Mr. ~is on the line.
　「~先生，已經幫您接上了。」

*There's no reply from room ~.
　Mr.~ doesn't answer.
　「~先生不在。」
　不可說成 Room ~ doesn't answer.

*I'll transfer your call to ~
　「我會幫您轉接給~」

*Could you dial XXX directly?
　「請您直撥 XXX 好嗎？」

*Thank you for calling.
　「謝謝您的電話。」

*I'm afraid you have the wrong number.
　「您撥的電話號碼好像不對。」

*Your party was cut off.
　「對方已經掛上電話了。」
　(cut off: 美語, hung up: 英語)

《音調練習》

1) Speaking.　May I help you?
2) I'll connect you.
3) You're connected now.
4) Go ahead, please.
5) Could you hold the line, please?
6) Mr. Brown is on the line.
7) Mr. Jones doesn't answer.
8) Would you like to leave a message?
9) I can hardly hear you.　Would you mind speaking a little louder?
10) There is no one by that name listed on the register.

《置換練習》

1) The line is busy.
　　　　　　out of order.
　　　　　　has been disconnected.

2) There's an outside call for you.
　　　　　a long distance call for you.
　　　　　an overseas call for you.

3) I'll connect you with the Front Desk.
　　　　　　　　　　Information.
　　　　　　　　　　Room Service.

《發音要訣》 this 的〔ð〕和 bath 的〔θ〕
 輕輕的把舌頭放在上齒與下齒之間然後發出聲音。拼音
 上雖然是相同的 th，但因單字的不同會發不同的音，請
 特別注意。

〔發音練習〕
that	〔ð æ t〕	thank	〔θ æ ŋ k〕
this	〔ð ɪ s〕	think	〔θ ɪ ŋ k〕
there	〔ð ɛ r〕	thought	〔θ ɔ t〕
those	〔ð o z〕	through	〔θ r u〕
these	〔ð i z〕	bath	〔b æ θ〕
though	〔ð o〕		

《英文會話要訣》〔讀書時，請大聲的唸〕
　　　對於英語寫作的書或是雜誌、報紙等，如果能夠大
 聲的唸出來，不但能夠培養英語的語感，同時對於培養
 單字及表現能力上都有很大的幫助。因為已經具有基礎
 的知識，對於有興趣的雜誌可以很容易的運用想像力來
 幫助理解。例如：海明威的小說（註：『老人與海』的
 作者），因為其文章深入淺出，非常適於閱讀，同時也
 有各種場面的會話，在此特別向讀者們推薦。當然有興
 趣的人，讀讀英文版的雜誌，也是很有幫助。

Lesson 9 指 示 路，地 點

　　以英語詳細說明道路或場所地點時，對初學者而言並不是一件容易的事，在指示道路時，不要太拘於細節，只要說明重點即可。

　　說明時常使用命令形，而使用的單字也都是常用的那幾句。因此，把道路的順序先在腦海中描繪一遍，再用正確的語句說出即可。

It's in the middle of the block.

《 **Dialogue Drill** 》　　*G*: Guest, *C*: Clerk

G: Excuse me.　Can you tell me how to get to the nearest subway station?

C: Of course, ma'am.　Go out the main exit, turn right, go two blocks, turn left, and you will see it in the middle of the next block.

G: Let's see...Go out the main exit, turn right, go two blocks, trun left, and it will be in the middle of the next block.

C: That's exactly right.

G: Thank you very much.

C: You're quite welcome, ma'am.

它在這條街區的中間。

《會話練習》　　*G*: 客人，　*C*: 飯店櫃檯人員

G: 對不起，能不能告訴我離這裏最近的地下鐵車站怎麼走？

C: 當然可以，女士。走出正門往右轉，過兩條街道後左轉，您可以看到它就在下一條街區中間。

G: 讓我想一下...走出正門往右轉，過兩條街道後左轉，它就在下一條街區的中間。

C: 完全正確。

G: 非常謝謝你。

C: 不客氣，女士。

《常用高頻率會話》

*Go straight.　Turn right.　Turn left.
「直走。右轉。左轉。」
在說明時是使用命令形，有時在前面加上 "please" 也可以。

*Go two blocks.
「過兩個街區。」
以英語介紹街道時，是以建築的區域來做為表示。

*It's on the (your) left (right).
「在您的左手邊（右手邊）。」

*It's in the middle of the block.
「它在街區的中間。」

*It's on the corner of~.
「它在~轉角。」

*Take the Mucha Line.
「搭乘木柵線。」

*Get off at the fourth stop.
「在第四站下車。」

*Transfer to the <u>Mu Cha Line</u> at <u>Chun-Hsiao</u> Station.
「在忠孝車站換乘木柵線。」

*It takes about three minutes on foot.
 It's about three minutes walk.
「走路約 3 分鐘路程。」

*The best way to get there is by taxi.
「到那裏搭計程車是最好的方法。」

- You'll see (find) the~.　（您將看到~）
  you'll come to~.　（您將來到~）

- follow the road　　　　（順著這條路）
  cross the street　　　　（過這條街）
  intersection (crossing)　（十字路口）
  one-way　　　　　　　（單程，單行道）
  round trip ticket　　　（來回車票）
  fork　　　　　　　　　（岔路）

- 關於 on, at, in 的使用方法
  I live <u>in</u> Tokyo.　　　　　　（表示地域）
  I'll meet you <u>at</u> the station.　（表示場所）
  I saw him <u>on</u> the street.　　　（表示地點）

- get in (out)　用在出入口，電梯等
- get on (off)　用在巴士，電車，汽車，電扶梯等

65

《音調練習》　＊劃線部分與錄音帶有所不同

1) You will find it in the middle of the next block.
2) Get off at the third bus stop.
3) Take a number five bus and get off at the second stop.
4) Go straight until you come to a traffic light.
5) Turn right at the second corner.
6) Turn left on Chung-Hsiao E. Road.
7) You will come to a large intersection.
8) It's next door to a school.
9) It's across the street from Plaza Hotel.
10) It's about five minutes walk from the staion.
11) Take the Tam Sui Line (淡水線) train bound for Taipei.
12) Take the Tam Sui Line (淡水線) train on track three.
13) Take the Shin Ten Line (新店線).
14) Transfer to the Shin Ten Line at Taipei Station.
15) Change to the subway at Taipei Station.
16) Change from the express to the local at Taipei Station.
17) Ride to the end of the line.
18) The fare is NT$ 120.
19) It's a two hour ride.
20) Go out the South Exit.
21) Turn to the right as you get off the train.
22) Turn left as you come out of the station.

《發音要訣》 would 的〔ʊ〕
將嘴唇呈圓形凸向前方，喉嚨發出「嗚」的聲音，不要發得太輕，要從喉嚨後面發出聲音。

〔發音練習〕
would	〔w ʊ d〕	wood	〔w ʊ d〕
could	〔k ʊ d〕	wool	〔w ʊ l〕
good	〔g ʊ d〕	woman	〔ˋw ʊ m ə n〕

《英文會話要訣》 〔抓到拍子時，就容易講得字正腔圓〕
　　發音要發得漂亮，除了注意發音及節奏之外，間隔及拍子也很重要。在長篇文章裡，如果拍子及換氣間隔不對時，會令對方聽不懂。因此，在遇到逗點及句點時，要停一拍，才不會誤使對方把兩句話聽成一句。在表示一整句的單字群時，必須一起唸完。你在看外國電影時也可以察覺到，不管說得多快，在每一個段落都會停一拍，再說下一段。

Lesson 10 飯店、餐廳內的介紹

　　飯店內的介紹，常常需要加上如何前往目的地的說明。在說明時，除了要注意簡潔之外，同時可親切地畫個地圖給客人。此外，在餐廳方面，可以附帶介紹餐飲的特色及營業時間等事項。

It's next to the elevators, ma'am.

《 **Dialogue Drill** 》　　*G*: Guest, *C*: Clerk

G: Excuse me.

C: Yes, ma'am.　May I help you?

G: Where can I make a telephone call?

C: Will you be making an outside call or a house call, ma'am?

G: Well, I'd like to make a house call first.　And then make an outside call.

C: I see.　The house phones are over there, next to the elevators, ma'am.　And the public phones are over there, opposite the house phones, ma'am.

G: Thank you very much.

C: You're welcome, ma'am.

女士，它在電梯旁邊。

《會話練習》　　**G**: 客人，　**C**: 飯店櫃檯人員

G:　對不起。

C:　是的，女士。您需要我效勞嗎？

G:　在那裏可以打電話呢？

C:　女士，請問您要打外線還是館內電話？

G:　嗯，我想先撥館內電話再撥外線。

C:　是的。女士，館內電話是在電梯旁邊。
　　　公用電話在那兒，是在館內電話的對面。

G:　非常謝謝你。

C:　不客氣，女士。

《常用高頻率會話》
*I'll show you the way.
　「我來為您帶路。」

*This way, please.
　「請往這邊。」

*It's next to the~.
　「它在~的旁邊。」

*It's over there.
　「它在那兒。」

*It's on the right (left).
　「它在右邊(左邊)。」

*It's on the third floor.
　「它在三樓。」

*It's in the basement.
　「它在地下室。」
　請注意 basement(地下室)的介系詞是使用 in 而不
　是 on。

*It's in the basement on level two.
　「它在地下室二樓。」

*It's back of~.
「在~的後面。」

*It's in front of~.
「在~的前面。」

*It's near the ~.
「在~的附近。」

*Go straight along the corridor.
「沿著走廊往前走。」

*It's around the corner.
「在轉角處周圍。」

*Go down (up) the stairs.
「請下樓(上樓)。」

*Take the elevator to the 5th floor.
「請搭電梯上五樓。」

*The rest room is over there.
「洗手間在那邊。」
有 toilet, wash room, lavatory, men's (women's) room
等的表示方法，rest room 是一般最常使用。

《音調練習》
1) Will you be making an outside call or a house call, ma'am?
2) The house phones are over there, next to the elevators, ma'am.
3) You'll find a flower shop in the arcade in the basement.
4) The banquet rooms are located in the South Wing (annex) on the second floor.
5) This elevator goes directly to the Sky Lounge Restaurant.
6) This elevator goes up as high as the twentieth floor.
   (到 20 樓為止)

《置換練習》
1) The coffee shop is <u>on the 3rd floor</u>.
                       on the 21st floor.
                       in the basement.

2) It's <u>near the elevator</u>.
        next to the elevator.
        in front of the elevator.

3) It's <u>one floor up</u>.
        two floors down.

《發音要訣》 what 的〔(h)w〕

　　輕輕的開口，如同從肚子中將氣發出來。嘴部的形狀就如同發「 WA 」一樣。一般而言發音沒有太大的困難。

〔發音練習〕

what	〔(h)w a t〕	while	〔(h)w a ɪ l〕
when	〔(h)w ɛ n〕	white	〔(h)w a ɪ t〕
where	〔(h)w ɛ r〕	why	〔(h)w a ɪ〕
which	〔(h)w ɪ tʃ〕	whether	〔(h)w ɛ ð ɚ〕

《英文會話要訣》〔**學習語言，如要更上層樓，要熟悉對方的文化背景**〕

　　到目前為止，在《英文會話要訣》之中，敘述了如何增進學習的速度及技巧，但是要記得人與人之間的溝通最重要的還是誠心及相互了解。同時為了理解對方，如能先了解對方的風俗、習慣、宗教等的文化背景也是非常重要的一個步驟。能夠了解對方基本的想法、相異的習慣，才是建立相互了解的第一步。因此，一方面學習英文，一方面可以平行的充實這方面的知識。如此的話，你的英語能力，一定可以更上一層樓。

PART II

依照各個業務的種類，學習各種場面的會話

Lesson 11 接受住宿的預約

在 PART I，各位讀者已學習了基本業務上的對應語句，在 PART II 中，我們將會學到實際業務上所發生的狀況及如何回答的相關語句。

關於預約的會話，由於客人直接來飯店預約的情況較少，所以實際業務上發生頻率是以「 Check In 」時較多。因此，要先了解這些單字及表現的方法。

When would you like to make reservations?

《 **Dialogue Drill** 》　　*G*: Guest, *R*: Reservation Clerk

R: Good morning.　Plaza Hotel.

G: Hello.　I'd like to make a reservation at your hotel for next month.

R: Certainly, sir.　Exactly when would you like to make reservations?

G: From the 15th to the 20th of next month.

R: Would you like a single or a double?

G: A single with bath.

R: I can confirm a single from the 15th to the 20th. May I have your name, sir?

G: Smith.　Larry Smith.

R: Thank you.　We will be looking forward to seeing you on the fifteenth of next month.

G: Thank you.　See you then.

R: Thank you for making a reservation with us, sir. Good-bye.

請問您要預訂何時的客房？

《會話練習》　　*G*：客人，*R*：訂房人員

R：　早安。<u>廣場</u>大飯店。

G：　早。

　　　我想預訂下個月的房間。

R：　好的，先生。

　　　您要預訂那一天呢？

G：　下個月 15 號到 20 號。

R：　您要訂單人房還是雙人房？

G：　附浴室的單人房。

R：　我幫您預定了 15 號到 20 號的單人房。

　　　先生，請問您的大名？

G：　史密斯。賴利‧史密斯。

R：　謝謝您。

　　　我們期待下個月 15 號見到您。

G：　謝謝，那麼下個月見。

R：　先生，謝謝您的預約。

　　　再見。

《常用高頻率會話》
*When would you like to make reservations?
「您要預訂什麼時候呢？」
For which date? (那一天呢？)在會話中也可使用這樣
簡單的表達語句。

*How many nights would you like to stay?
「您預定住幾個晚上？」
也可使用 For how many nights? 的表達。

*How many guests will there be in your party?
「您們有幾位？」

*Would you like a twin or a double?
「您要訂兩張單人床的房間還是雙人床？」
・ What kind of room would you like?
「您要訂什麼樣的房間？」
・ Which kind of room would you prefer, a twin or a double?
這句話是更正確的表現。

*Let me check if we have a twin room available on those dates.
「讓我查一下那個時候是否有兩張單人床的房間。」
・ I'll check our room availability.
「我查看一下我們是否有空房間。」

78

*May I have your phone number, please?
「能否能給我您的聯絡電話？」
　・ Where can we contact you?
　・ At what number can you be reached?
這兩句意思一樣，也常被使用。

*At what time will you be arriving?
「您預定將於何時到達？」

*We will be looking forward to seeing you.
We look forward to serving you.
「我們期待與您見面。」

《單字與發音》
reservation 〔‚ r ɛ z ə ˋ v e ʃ ə n〕（名）預約，指定
confirm 〔k ə n ˋ f ɝ m〕（動）確定，確認事項
available 〔ə ˋ v e l ə b l〕（形）可以提供，可利用的
book 〔b ʊ k〕（動）登記，預定
rate 〔r e t〕（名）比率，價格
deposit 〔d ɪ ˋ p ɑ z ɪ t〕（名）銀行存款，保証金
advance 〔ə d ˋ v æ n s〕（名）進步，訂金(先付款)
condition 〔k ə n ˋ d ɪ ʃ ə n〕（名）狀態，身分，條件

79

1) What kind of room would you like?
2) Exactly when would you like to make reservations?
3) I can confirm a single from the 15th to the 20th.
4) We will be looking forward to seeing you on the 15th.
5) Thank you for making reservations with us, sir.
6) What kind of room would you prefer, a twin or a double?
7) We have a single reserved for you.
8) May I reconfirm your departure time?
9) May I have your phone number, please?
10) Would you like a room with a sea view or a mountain view?

《置換練習》

1) How many <u>nights would you like to stay</u>?
        guests will there be in your party?
        more days would you like to extend?

2) At what time will <u>you be arriving</u>?
        it be convenient for you?
        number can you be reached?

3) I hope you <u>enjoy your stay with us</u>.
        find what you're looking for.
        have a nice flight home.

《請翻譯成英文》

1) **G**: 我想預訂下個月的房間。
   C: 好的，從那一天開始呢？
2) **G**: 我想預訂房間。
   C: 謝謝，先生。您要預訂那一天呢？
3) **C**: 您要什樣的房間？
   G: 一間兩張單人床的房間(Twin)。
4) **C**: 您要住幾晚呢？
   G: 四晚。
5) **G**: 面對海邊和背對的單人房價格相差多少？
   C: 大約差 1,500 元。

〔 **Answers** 〕

1) **G**: I'd like to make a reservation for next month.
   C: Certainly, sir.   From what day would you like to make reservations for?
2) **G**: I'd like to make a reservation.
   C: Thank you, sir.   For which date, sir?
3) **C**: What kind of room would you like to have?
   G: I would like to have a twin.
4) **C**: How many nights will you be staying?
   G: Four nights.
5) **G**: What is the rate difference of a single with a sea view and a rear view.
   C: The difference is about NT$1,500.

Lesson 12　住 宿 客 人 Check In

　　當客人到達飯店時，辦理一連串的住宿登記手續稱為 Check in，而負責此業務的部門是櫃檯接待(Front Reception)。業務的重點是確認客人是否有預約及住宿的條件等，同時請客人填寫住宿登記卡。

May I have your name, ma'am?

《 **Dialogue Drill** 》　　*G*: Guest, *C*: Clerk

C: Good afternoon, ma'am.　May I help you?

G: Yes.　I have a reservation here for a room.

C: May I have your name, ma'am?

G: Butterfield.　Mary Butterfield.

C: Excuse me, ma'am.　How do you spell your name?

G: B-U-T-T-E-R-F-I-E-L-D.

C: Butterfield.　Thank you, ma'am.　Just a moment, please... Yes, ma'am.　We have a single with bath for you until next Wednesday.　Could you fill out this card, please?

G: Of course....　Here you are...

C: Thank you, ma'am.　Your room is 502 on the fifth floor.　The bellboy will take your bags and show you to your room.　Please enjoy your stay with us.

G: Thank you.

能否請教您的大名？

《會話練習》　　G: 客人，　C: 飯店櫃檯人員

C: 女士，午安。能為您服務嗎？

G: 是的。我預訂了一間房間。

C: 女士，請教您的大名？

G: 柏特菲爾德。瑪麗・柏特菲爾德。

C: 對不起，女士。請問您的名字怎麼拼？

G: B-U-T-T-E-R-F-I-E-L-D。

C: Butterfield(柏特菲爾德)。謝謝您，女士。
　　請稍等一下…。是的，女士。我們為您準備
　　了一間單人房間附浴室直到下禮拜三。請您
　　填寫這張卡好嗎？

G: 當然好的。填寫好了，在這裡。

C: 謝謝您，女士。
　　您的房間是 5 樓的 502 號房。
　　服務生將會為您提行李，並且帶您到房間。
　　希望您住得愉快。

G: 謝謝。

《常用高頻率會話》

*May I have your initials, please?
「能否請教您大名的縮寫？」
initial〔ɪ`nɪʃəl〕請注意這發音。如果是複
數時必須加上 "s"。

*How do you spell your name, ma'am?
「能否請教您的大名怎麼拼？」

*Could you fill out this form, please?
「請填一下這張表，好嗎？」
· Will you please write your name in the register?
「能否請您將大名寫在這張住宿登記卡上？」
住宿登記卡稱為 register card， 在「 Check In 」時
，務必請客人登記。

*Let me check our files.
「讓我查一下檔案。」

*Your reservation is for a single for two nights.
「您是預約一間單人房 2 個晚上。」

*Do you have a reservation with us, sir?
「先生，您有預約嗎？」

*It's NT$4,500 a night, plus a 10% tax and service charge.

「一晚新台幣 4,500 元，外加 10%的營業稅及服務費。」

include (包含)，也可使用 exclude (除外) 來代替。

• It's NT$4,500 a night including tax and service charge.

「內含稅及服務費，一晚是新台幣 4,500 元。」

*The bellboy will take your bags and show you to your room.

「行李員會將行李搬到您的房間。」

*Please enjoy your stay with us.

「希望您住得愉快。」

這是一句常用的語句，有時可將 please 改為 I hope you will~.

*How would you like to make the (your) payment?

「您要怎麼付款？」

《單字與發音》

registration 〔ˏrɛdʒɪˋstreʃən〕(名) 記入，登記

include 〔ɪnˋklud〕 (動) 包含，放進(帳單

exclude 〔ɪkˋsklud〕 (動) 除外，不放進

payment 〔ˋpemənt〕 (名) 付款，報酬

bill 〔bɪl〕 (名) 帳單，請款單

1) May I have your initials, please?
2) Do you have a reservation with us, sir?
3) We have a single with bath for you until next Wednesday, ma'am.
4) We can give you a double with bath for <u>NT$5,500</u> a night.
5) It's <u>NT$4,500</u> a night, plus a 10% tax and service charge.
6) How would you like to make the payment?
7) Your room is 502 on the fifth floor.
8) The bellboy will take your bags and show you to your room.
9) I hope you enjoy your stay with us.
10) Please enjoy your stay with us.

《置換練習》

1) How do you spell your <u>first name, please?</u>
         middle name, please?
         last name, please?

2) Could you <u>sign here, please?</u>
     fill out the form, please?
     write your name in the register, please?

3) May I ask <u>the name again, please?</u>
     if he is with a tour?
     when he checked in?
     when you made the reservation?

《請翻譯成英文》

1) *C*: 先生，您有訂房嗎？
   G: 有的，上個月。
2) *C*: 能否請教您的大名？
   G: B-U- double T-E-R-F-I-E-L-D
3) *G*: 這貴重品怎麼處理？
   C: 如果您希望的話，可以寄放在櫃檯的寄放箱。
4) *G*: 一定是弄錯了。之前我打電話給你們時，你們確認我的房間是附浴室的雙人房。
   C: 那我查一下記錄，請稍待一下。
5) *G*: 可以使用信用卡嗎？
   C: 可以，但是我們只能使用 A、B、C公司的信用卡。

〔 **Answers** 〕

1) *C*: Do you have a reservation with us, sir?
   G: Yes, I made it last month.
2) *C*: How do you spell your name, sir?
   G: B-U- double T-E-R-F-I-E-L-D.
3) *G*: Where can I keep my valuables?
   C: You may keep them in the safety deposit box here at the Front, if you wish.
4) *G*: There must be some mistake. You confirmed a double with bath for me when I called.
   C: Let me check our files. Just a moment, please.
5) *G*: May I use my credit card?
   C: Yes, sir. But we only accept A, B, and C.

Lesson 13 帶客人至房間

在飯店的業務中，帶客人到房間是行李員(Bell boy)的工作，負責確認客人行李的個數及房間號碼，同時必須介紹並說明房間的設備，讓客人了解。

How many bags do you have?

《 **Dialogue Drill** 》   *G*: Guest, *B*: Bellboy

B: Welcome to the Plaza Hotel, ma'am.   Are these all your bags?

G: No, mine are the two large blue suitcases over there.

B: Certainly, ma'am...   May I have your room key, please?   Room 310.   Would you please follow me, ma'am.   The elevators are over there.   This way, please.   To the left.   Here is your room, 310.   (He opens the door.)

G: It's very nice.

B: Thank you, ma'am. This is the air conditioning control.   Shall I hang your a dress in the closet, ma'am?

G: Yes, please.   Thank you.

B: Your door locks automatically.   Please take your key with you when you go out.

G: I will.   Thank you.

您有幾件行李？

《會話練習》　　*G*: 客人，　*B*: 行李員
　　B: 歡迎女士光臨<u>廣場</u>大飯店。這些都是您的行李
　　　　嗎？
　　G: 不是的。我的行李是在那裡的兩個藍色大行李
　　　　箱。
　　B: 好的。請把鑰匙交給我好嗎？
　　　　310 號房。
　　　　女士，請跟我來。
　　　　電梯就在那裡。請走這邊。
　　　　您的房間 310 就在左邊。(服務生打開房門)。
　　G: 這房間很好。
　　B: 謝謝您，女士。
　　　　這是空氣調節的開關，女士。
　　　　我可以將您的衣服掛在衣櫃裡嗎？
　　G: 是的，麻煩你。謝謝。
　　B: 您的房門會自動上鎖，外出時請隨身攜帶鑰
　　　　匙。
　　G: 我會的，謝謝你。

《常用高頻率會話》
*How many bags do you have?
「您有幾件行李？」

*Are these all your bags?
「這裡的行李是您的嗎？」

*Is this your baggage?
「這是您的行李嗎？」

*Is this everything, sir?
「您的行李全部都在這邊嗎？」

*Would you please follow me?
「請跟我來。」

*Please take your key with you when you go out, sir.
「您出門時，請帶著您的鑰匙。」

*If there are any problems, please call the Front Desk.
「如果有任何問題，請詢問櫃檯。」

*Is there anything else I can do for you?
「如有什麼需要請吩咐。」

*The emergency exit is over there.
「緊急出口是在這邊。」

〔關於電梯〕
*Going up (down).
　「(電梯)上行，下行」

*Which (what) floor, sir?
　「先生，您要到幾樓？」

*After you, sir.
　「先生，請先。」

〔關於寄存貴重物品〕
*Is there anything valuable or breakable in your bag?
　「是否有任何貴重的東西，或是易破碎的物品，在
　　您的袋子之中？」

*You may keep your valuables at the Front Desk.
　「有貴重品的話，可寄放在櫃檯。」

《單字與發音》
baggage	〔`bægɪdʒ〕	(名)行李　(美語)
luggage	〔`lʌgɪdʒ〕	(名)行李　(英語)
emergency	〔ɪ`mɝdʒənsɪ〕	(名)緊急時
valuables	〔`væljuəblz〕	(名)貴重品(複數)
breakables	〔`brekəblz〕	(名)易損壞之物(複數)
closet	〔`klɑzɪt〕	(名)抽屜，衣櫃
automatically	〔ˌɔtə`mætɪkəlɪ〕	(副)自動地

《音調練習》
1) The elevators are over there.
2) Your door locks automatically.
3) If you are leaving the hotel, please leave your room key at the Front Desk.
4) Please help yourself to the things in the refrigerator.
5) It will be added to your bill, automatically.
6) You have independent control of the air-conditioning.
7) The controls for the lighting and stereo unit are located on the bedside console.
8) If you have any questions about the room you will find English instructions in the stationery folder.
9) You will find information about the hotel in English in the stationery folder.
10) The emergency exit is over there.

《置換練習》
1) Could you change your money at the exchange counter?
        dial 12 for laundry service?
        ask at the Front Desk?

2) It's open from nine to five.
        from 7:00 to 9:30 for breakfast.
        from 11:30 to 3:00 for lunch.
        from 5:30 to 8:30 for dinner.

《請翻譯成英文》

1) *G*: 緊急出口在那裡？
   B: 緊急出口在各樓層走廊的兩端。

2) *G*: 對不起。請問咖啡廳幾點開始營業？
   B: 咖啡廳的營業時間是上午 7 點到晚上 11 點。

3) *G*: 對不起，那裡可以買到明信片？
   B: 明信片在地下層商店街可以買得到。

4) *G*: 我想吃日本料理，可否推薦一間好一點的餐廳。
   B: 我可以推薦 32 樓的日本料理餐廳。他們提供的餐點非常可口。

〔 **Answers** 〕

1) *G*: Where are the emergency exits located?
   B: You will find an emergency exit at both sides of each hallway on every floor.

2) *G*: Excuse me.　What time is the coffee shop open?
   B: It's open from 7 a.m. to 11 p.m., sir.

3) *G*: Excuse me.　Where can I buy postcards?
   B: Postcards can be found in the arcade in the basement.

4) *G*: We'd like to try some Japanese food.　Can you recommend a good restaurant?
   B: The Japanese restaurant on the thirty-second floor offers delicious dishes.

Lesson 14 會 計 （ 買 單 ）

　　算帳、買單的出納部門，英語稱作 Cashier，因為日常的業務是處理金錢，所以對於數字的唸法必須特別注意。此外，最近使用信用卡的客人也很多，因此相關的會話，也請一併學起來。通常兌換外幣也會在這個部門處理。

Your bill comes to NT$41,360.

《 **Dialogue Drill** 》　　　G: Guest, C: Cashier
G: Excuse me.　I want to pay my bill.
C: Yes, sir.　May I ask your name and room number, sir?
G: Robert Green, room twelve forty-two.
C: Just a moment, please.　The cashier will have your bill ready in a moment...
　　Here you are, sir.
G: Let's see...NT$41,360.......
　　Here's NT$50,000.
C: Thank you, sir.

　　. . . . .
　　Here's your change and receipt.
G: Thank you.
C: Thank you, sir.　Good-bye.

您的帳單是 NT$41,360。

《會話練習》　　**G**: 客人，　**C**: 飯店出納人員

G: 對不起。我要付帳。

C: 是的，先生。
　　請問先生您的大名及房間號碼？

G: Robert Green(羅伯葛林)， 1242 號房。

C: 請稍等一下。
　　出納員馬上會準備好您的帳單。
　　　　先生，這是您的帳單。

G: 讓我看看... NT$41,360......
　　這是 NT$50,000。

C: 謝謝您，先生。
　　　. . . . .
　　這是找錢及收據。

G: 謝謝。

C: 謝謝您，先生。再見。

《常用高頻率會話》

*May I have your room key, please?
「請把房間鑰匙交給我好嗎？」
在結帳時，通常會先確認房間鑰匙。

*I'll draw up your bill for you.
 I'll calculate that for you.
「我會把帳單算給您。」

*Your bill comes (up) to $41,360 .
「您的帳單是 41,360 元。」

*Here is your change of $3,750.
「找您 3,750 元。」

*Cash or credit card?
「您付帳是用現金還是信用卡？」

*May I have your credit card?
「能否將您的卡片交給我？」

*I'm afraid we don't accept X X X card.
「對不起，我們不接受 XXX 卡」

*The balance due is $800.
「(與預付的金額)差額是 800 元。」

*Thank you for staying with us.
 I hope you enjoyed your stay here, sir.
  「謝謝您住在我們這兒。希望令您滿意。」

*Our check out time is twelve noon, sir.
  「 Check out 時間是 12 點。」

*Would you like to talk with our assistant manager?
  「您要與我們副理說話嗎？」

〔有關 Check out 的會話〕
*I'll send a bellboy to your room for your baggage.
  「我會派行李員去您房間拿行李。」

*How much luggage do you have?
  「您有幾件行李？」

*I've come for your bags.
  「我會去提您的行李。」

《單字與發音》
calculate	〔`kælkjə,let〕	(動)	計算，評價
draw up	〔`drɔ,ʌp〕	(動+副)	作出，寫出，開出
change	〔tʃendʒ〕	(名)	找錢，零錢
accept	〔ək`sɛpt〕	(動)	接受，承認
receipt	〔rɪ`sit〕	(名)	收據，收下
balance	〔`bæləns〕	(名)	差額
note	〔nɑt〕	(名)	〔商〕紙幣

《音調練習》
1) We'll have your bill ready for you tomorrow morning.
2) I'll draw up your bill for you.
3) It will take about three minutes to prepare your bill.
4) Your bill comes to NT$52,000 including tax and service charge.
5) Here is your change of NT$4,250.
6) Could you sign this card and pay your bill, sir?
7) I'm afraid we don't accept the ABC card.
8) Our check out time is twelve noon, sir.
9) Thank you for staying with us.
10) Please stay with us the next time you come to Taiwan.

《置換練習》
1) May I ask your name and room number, sir?
　　　　　　what time will be convenient?
　　　　　　how many bags you have?

2) The cashier will have your bill ready in a moment.
　　　　　　　　　　　　　　　　　by then.
　　　　　　　　　　　　　　　　　tomorrow morning.

3) Here is your card.
　　　　　　receipt.
　　　　　　card and receipt.
　　　　　　change and receipt.

《請翻譯成英語》
1) **G**: 可以使用美國運通卡嗎？
   C: 可以，請填一下這張表。
2) **C**: 請在這帳單簽名並付款。差額是 1,800 元。
   G: 我昨天已經給了飯店住宿券,其他的東西每次也付了現金,現在為什麼又要付呢？
   C: 這是因為飯店住宿券是不包含稅金及服務費。
   G: 我明白了,這些我付。

〔 **Answers** 〕
1) **G**: Can I use my American Express credit card?
   C: Yes, sir.   Could you please fill out this form?
2) **C**: Could you sign this card and pay your bill, sir?
   The balance due is NT$1,800.
   G: I gave you hotel coupons yesterday, and I paid
   every bill by cash.   Why do I owe you anything
   now?
   C: The Hotel coupon states that it does not include
   tax and service charge, sir.
   G: I see.   Here you are.

Lesson 15 介紹各種事項（1）

　　櫃檯接待人員的業務可分為回答 (1) 住宿客人提出的問題 (2) 訪客詢問有關住宿客人的問題 (3) 準備住宿或是準備要預約客人的問題等三大部分。訪客的問題主要包括詢問房間號碼、物品轉交、留言等。

Mr. Green is in Room #312.

《 Dialogue Drill 》　　*V*: Visitor, *C*: Clerk

C: Good evening, sir.　May I help you?

V: Yes, please.　Could you tell me what room Mr. Green is in?

C: Is he with a tour?

V: Yes, but I don't know the name of it.

C: Excuse me , sir.　May I ask what his name is again, please?

V: Green, Robert Green.

C: Thank you, sir.　Just a moment, please....
Yes.　Mr. Robert Green is in room three twelve.

V: Where can I call him?

C: You may use the house (hotel) phone.
It's over there by the elevator, sir.

V: Thank you very much.

C: You're welcome, sir.

葛 林 先 生 住 在 *312* 號 房。

《會話練習》　　*V*: 客人，　*C*: 飯店櫃檯人員
C: 先生，晚安。需要我效勞嗎？
V: 是的。您可以告訴我 Mr.Green(葛林先生)的房間
　　是哪一間嗎？
C: 請問他是跟隨旅行團嗎？
V: 是的。但是我不知道旅行團的名字。
C: 對不起，先生。可不可以再告訴我一次他的名
　　字呢？
V: Green(葛林)， Robert Green(羅伯·葛林)。
C: 謝謝您，先生。請稍等一下。
　　是的。 Robert Green 住在 312 號房。
V: 請問我可以在哪裡打電話給他呢？
C: 先生，您可以使用館內專用電話。
　　電話就在電梯旁邊。
V: 非常謝謝你。
C: 不客氣。

《常用高頻率會話》

*Mr. Green is in Room #312.
「葛林先生的房間是 312。」

*Will you be making an outside call or a house call, ma'am?
「您是要撥外線，還是要撥館內電話？」

*For a house call, first dial 8 and then the room number.
「撥館內電話時，先撥 8 後再撥房間號碼。」

*We have no guest under that name.
「我們沒有叫那個名字的客人。」

*We have a reservation for him, but he still hasn't checked in.
「他已預約，但是他尚未住進來。」

*He (Mr. ~) checked out yesterday.
「他（~ 先生）已經於昨天離開了。」

*We will keep it for Mr. Green.
「我們會替葛林先生保管它。」

*We will hand it to Mr. Green.
「我們會交給葛林先生。」

〔接受客人留言等的處理〕
*Would you like to leave a message for him?
　「您需要留言嗎？」

*I'll repeat your message.
　「我重覆您的留言。」

*Here is a message (letter) for you from Mr.～.
　「～先生給您一份留言。」

*There is no message (letter) for you.
　「沒有您的留言。」

*Shall I page him?
　「需要我傳呼他嗎？」

《單字與發音》
deliver 〔dɪ`lɪvɚ〕　　　　　(動) 送達，交給
message 〔`mɛsɪdʒ〕　　　 (名) 留言，傳話
directly 〔də`rɛktlɪ〕　　　 (副) 直接的，一直
page 　　〔pedʒ〕　　　　　(動) 傳呼

103

《音調練習》
1) Mr. Green is in Room #312.
2) Shall we put it on your bill, sir?
3) I'll send someone up right away, sir.
4) I'll have the hotel operator page him in the lobby then, sir.
5) It's over there by the elevator.
6) We have no guest under that name.
7) Here is a message for you from Mr. Brown.
8) There is no letter for you.

《置換練習》
1) Would you like to leave a message for him?
                   to have him paged?
                   me to check if he has a reservation
                                           with us?
                   me to check if he has already checked in?

2) Will you be making a house call or an outside call?
                      a long distance call?
                      a local call?
                      a direct call?

3) There's an arcade in the basement.
            a barber shop in the arcade in the basement.
            a Sushi Bar on the third floor.
            a flower shop next to the Cloakroom.

《請翻譯成英語》

1) **G**: 請問我可以在哪裡留言呢？
   C: 櫃檯有提供留言箋。
2) **G**: 請問我可以在房間裡打越洋電話嗎？
   C: 可以，先生。您可以請接線生為您接越洋電話。
3) **G**: 請問有我的信嗎？
   C: 有的，先生。這裡有您的信。
   (沒有，先生。沒有您的信。)
4) **G**: 可為我發這份電報嗎？
   C: 可以，先生。我們可將費用記在您的帳單上嗎？

〔 **Answers** 〕

1) **G**: Where can I leave a message?
   C: Message slips are available at the Front Desk.
2) **G**: Can I make an overseas call from my room?
   C: Yes, sir. Please place your call through the switchboard operator, sir.
3) **G**: Is there any mail for me?
   C: Yes, sir. Here is a letter for you.
   (No, sir. There is no letter for you.)
4) **G**: Could you send this telegram for me, please?
   C: Yes, sir. Shall we put it on your bill, sir?

Lesson 16　介 紹 各 種 事 項 (2)

　　對住宿的客人提供的各種服務中，常包括介紹購物、觀光及館內介紹等。如果是較常用到的項目，許多飯店都會事先準備說明卡片，方便客人瞭解。

What would you like to buy?

《 Dialogue Drill 》　　*G*: Guest, *C*: Clerk

G: Excuse me.　Will you tell me where I can do some shopping?

C: Yes, ma'am.　There's an arcade in the basement.

G: No.　I want to go outside the hotel.

C: I see, ma'am.　Is there anything in particular which you would like to buy?

G: As a matter of fact, yes!　I'd like to buy a chinese dress and some wooden dolls.

C: A chinese dress and wooden dolls?　I suggest that you go to a large department store, ma'am. Just a moment, please....
Here you are, ma'am.　Just give this card to the taxi driver and he will take you to the Plaza Department Store.

G: Thank you very much.

C: You're welcome, ma'am.

您想要買什麼東西？

《會話練習》　　G: 客人，　C: 飯店櫃檯人員

G: 對不起。
你可否告訴我哪裡可以購物嗎？

C: 可以，女士。地下一樓有商店街。

G: 不是，我想要到旅館外面。

C: 我明白了，女士。
您想購買什麼特別的東西嗎？

G: 事實上，是的。我想要買一件中國式旗袍和一些木製娃娃。

C: 一件中國式旗袍和一些木製娃娃嗎？我建議您到大的百貨公司去買。
請稍等一下，
女士，這張卡給您。
您只要把這張卡交給計程車司機，他會載你到 Plaza 百貨公司。

G: 非常謝謝你。

C: 不客氣，女士。

《常用高頻率會話》

*There's an arcade in the basement.
「地下樓有商店街。」

*What would you like to buy?
What are you looking for?
「您想買些什麼？」

*I suggest that you go to a large department store.
「我建議您到大型的百貨公司。」

*You can purchase (buy) things duty free at ~.
「在~，您可購買到免稅的物品。」

*Just give this card to the taxi driver and he will take
you to the XXX Store.
「只要把這張卡交給計程車司機，他會帶您到 XXX
店。」

*If you plan to come back to the hotel by taxi, give this
card to the driver and he will bring you back to this
hotel.
「如果您要回到飯店，只要把這張卡片交給計程車
司機，他會帶您回到飯店。」

*Here is the name and address of a good one.
「這些是優良商店的店名及地址。」

*The postage rate is NT$3.5 for a postcard, and NT$5 for a letter.

「明信片是台幣$3.5，平信是 5 元。」

*For special delivery it's NT$7 more.

「限時信是多加 7 元。」

*To send it registered mail you must go to the post office.

「掛號信是必須要到郵局才能交寄。」

*For city bus tours, please sign up at the counter over there.

「如果要搭乘市內觀光巴士，請在那邊的櫃檯辦理。」

《單字與發音》

department store〔dɪˋpartmənt͵stor〕百貨公司
duty free shop 〔ˋdjutɪ͵friˋʃap〕 免稅店
special delivery〔ˋspɛʃəl dɪˋlɪvərɪ〕快遞、限時
registered mail 〔ˋrɛdʒɪstəd͵mel〕 掛號信件
parcel post 〔ˋparsl͵post〕 郵局小包

1) What would you like to buy?
2) What are you looking for?
3) Here is the name and address of a good one.
4) I hope that you'll be able to find something you like.
5) Have a nice day.
6) The postage rate is <u>NT$3.5</u> for a post card, and <u>NT$5</u> for a letter.
7) For special delivery it's <u>NT$7</u> more.
8) To send it registered mail you must go to the post office.

《置換練習》
1) I suggest that you go to <u>a large department store.</u>
<u>Kwang Hwa Market</u> for electrical and computer appliances.
the <u>National Palace Museum.</u>
<u>Yang Ming Shan</u> to see the cherry blossoms.
<u>Chung Hsiao E. Road</u> for shopping.

玉市　(Jade Market)
夜市　(Night Market)

《請翻譯成英語》
1) **G**: 對不起。請問如何到松山機場轉運站？
   C: 你可以搭乘捷運。坐木柵線，往中山國中方向，在中山國中下車。下車後，走一下馬上就可以到了。
2) **G**: 對不起。能否告訴我，故宮博物館怎麼走？
   C: 你知道怎麼去台北車站嗎？
   G: 我知道。
   C: 從台北車站，有 304 的巴士可以到。

〔 **Answers** 〕
1) **G**: Excuse me.　How do you get to the Song-Shan Air Terminal?
   C: You can use the MRTS.　Take the Mu Cha Line bound for Chung Shan School, and get off at Chung Shan School Station.
   It's a short walk from the station.
2) **G**: Excuse me.　Could you tell me how to get to the National Palace Museum?
   C: Do you know how to get to Taipei Station?
   G: Yes, I do.
   C: From Taipei Station, there is a No. 304 bus to the National Palace Museum.

Lesson 17 客 房 部

　　負責客房的管理及清潔服務的部門，通常都稱爲(Housekeeping) 客房部。同時也接受客人送洗的衣服及負責處理客房內遺失物品等業務。此外，對於提供客房餐飲 (Room Service)，大多數的飯店是由 F&B (Food & Beverage) 餐飲部門來負責。

We will deliver it by tomorrow noon.

《 Dialogue Drill 》　　*G*: Guest, *H*: Housekeeper

H:　Good morning.　Housekeeping.　May I help you?

G:　Yes, I'd like to know about your laundry service hours.

H:　If your laundry is received before 10 a.m., we will deliver it to your room by 10 p.m. the same day. If we receive it before 3 p.m., we'll get it back to you by noon the next day, sir.

G:　What are your rates?

H:　The rate chart is contained in the stationery folder in your dresser drawer, sir.

G:　I see... Well, would you please send someone to room 604 to pick up some laundry for me?

H:　Yes, sir.　The roommaid will be there in a few minutes, sir.

G:　Thank you.

H:　You're welcome, sir.

我們將會在明天中午送還給你。

《會話練習》　　G: 客人，　H: 客房服務人員
H: 早安，客房管理部。需要我效勞嗎？
G: 是的。
　　我想要知道你們洗衣服務的時間。
H: 先生，如果您的衣服在早上 10 點送洗，當天晚
　　上 10 點，我們就可以把洗好的衣服送到您房間
　　。如果在下午 3 點以前，我們收到您送洗的衣服
　　，我們將在隔天中午送還給您。
G: 那麼費用呢？
H: 先生，在您的化粧台的抽屜裡，有一本迎賓手
　　冊，收費表就在裡面。
G: 我明白了。請你派人到 604 號房收取我要送洗
　　的衣服，好嗎？
H: 是的，先生。
　　客房服務生將會在幾分鐘內到您房間。
G: 謝謝你。
H: 不客氣，先生。

《常用高頻率會話》

*The laundry forms are in the stationery folder in the desk in your room, sir.
「洗衣單是放在您房間桌子抽屜內的文件夾之中。」

*Please fill out the form.
「請填寫洗衣單。」

*For laundry service, dial 6 and you will get House-keeping.
「如需要洗衣服務，請撥 6 號即可接通客房部。」

*The roommaid will be there in a few minutes. We will send someone immediately.
「負責的人會馬上到。」
「我們會馬上派人過去。」

*We will deliver it to your room by tomorrow noon.
「我們將於明天中午前送到您的房間。」

*If you are in a hurry we have a two hour quick service.
「如果您很急，我們有 2 小時快洗的服務。」

*There is an extra charge of 50% for quick service.
「快洗服務會增加 50%的服務費。」

〔有關於客室清掃〕
*Housemaid.　May I clean your room?
　「這裡是客房部，能否打掃您的房間？」

*What time would be convenient for you?
　「什麼時候，您較方便？」

*I'll have the engineer look at it right away.
　「我會請工程師馬上過去看一下。」

*I'm sorry to disturb you.
　「很抱歉打擾您。」

《單字和發音》
stationery 〔`ste ʃ ə , n ɛ r ɪ〕 (名) 文具
folder 〔`f o l d ɚ〕 (名) 書類夾
laundry 〔`l ɔ n d r ɪ〕 (名) 洗衣物
quick 〔k w ɪ k〕 (形) 短時間的、迅速的
convenient 〔k ə n `v i n j ə n t〕 (形) 方便的，適切的
disturb 〔d ɪ `s t ɚ b〕 (動) 妨害 (睡眠)、擾亂

《音調練習》
1) Please fill out the form.
2) For laundry service, dial 6 and you will get House-
keeping.
3) The roommaid will be there in a few minutes.
4) May I clean your room?
5) What time would be convenient for you?
6) We have a two hour quick service.

《置換練習》
1) I'm very sorry to disturb you.
　　　　　　　　for the inconvenience.
　　　　　　　　to bother you.
　　　　　　　　to interrupt you.

2) There is a vending machine on each floor.
　　　　　　no laundry service on Sundays.
　　　　　　some shoeshine paper in the closet.
　　　　　　an extra charge for quick service.

3) We will send someone immediately.
　　　　　deliver it to your room.
　　　　　bring it as soon as possible.

《請翻譯成英語》

1) **G**: 請問我可以在房間裡使用我的吹風機嗎？
   我的吹風機是外國製的。

   H: 不可以，女士。使用之前你必須要先接個變電器。

2) **G**: 請問怎樣才能將我的衣服送洗呢？

   H: 先生，你可以在你房間的化粧台的抽屜裡找到迎賓
   手冊，手冊裡附有衣服乾洗的表格及收費表。

3) **G**: 我想要一些冰塊，請你送一些來好嗎？

   H: 我們都請客人直接到電梯旁的製冰機拿取冰塊。

〔 **Answers** 〕

1) **G**: Will I be able to use my hair dryer in my room?
   It's a foreign brand.

   H: No, ma'am.   You will have to use an adaptor.

2) **G**: How do I get a suit cleaned?

   H: You'll find a dry cleaning form and the rates in
   the stationery folder in the desk in your room,sir.

3) **G**: I'd like to have some ice.   Could you bring me
   some?

   H: We ask the guests to use the ice-dispenser next to
   the elevator hall.

Lesson 18 餐 飲（帶位）

　　帶位一般都是由較資深且穿著正式的領班服務人員來擔任。但如能夠把它熟記，相信會更了解業務的流程。此外，在接受預約時也是以相同的語句來做說明。

I'll show you to your table.

《 **Dialogue Drill** 》　　*G*: Guest, *H*: Head Waiter

H: Welcome to the <u>Plaza</u> Restaurant. How are you this afternoon?

G: Thank you. I'm just fine.

H: Are you by yourself?

G: Yes, just myself.

H: I'll show you to your table. This way, please.... Is this alright?

G: Well, could I sit over there by the window, instead?
As I would like to have a view of mountain.

H: I'm afraid that table is reserved, ma'am. How about this one?

G: This will be fine.

H: Please take a seat, ma'am.

G: Thank you.

H: A waiter will come to take your order. Just a moment, please. I hope you enjoy your meal.

讓我來帶位。

《會話練習》　　G: 客人，　H: 領班

H: 歡迎光臨廣場餐廳。
　　今天下午您好嗎？
G: 謝謝你。我很好。
H: 只有您一位嗎？
G: 是的，只有我自己一個人。
H: 讓我帶您到桌位。請走這邊...
　　這個位子可以嗎？
G: 請問我可不可以換到窗戶旁邊的位子
　　呢？
　　因為我想觀賞山邊的景色。
H: 對不起，那個位子已經被人預訂了，女士。
　　您覺得這個位子如何呢？
G: 這個位子可以。
H: 女士，請坐。
G: 謝謝你。
H: 服務生會過來請您點菜。請稍等。
　　希望您用餐愉快。

《常用高頻率會話》
*How many persons, please?
　「請問有幾位？」

*A table for two?
　Just for the two of you?
　「您們二位嗎？」

*Are you by yourself?
　「您一位嗎？」

*Do you have a reservation with us, sir?
　「您有預約嗎？」

*Where would you prefer to sit?
　「您想要坐在那裏？」

*I'll show you to your table.
　「讓我來帶位。」

*I'll show you to a table in just a moment.
　「我會馬上帶您入座，請稍等。」

*Please wait to be escorted to a table.
　「請稍等，等一下會帶您入座。」

*This way , please.　(Come this way, sir.)
　「請往這邊。」

*Is this table alright?
　「這個位子可以嗎？」

*How about this table?
　「這個桌位，您滿意嗎？」

*I'm afraid that table is reserved.
　「對不起，那桌已經被預約了。」

*We have no open tables (at the moment).　Would you please wait about five minutes?
　「現在因為客滿，請稍等 5 分鐘左右？」

*A waiter will come to take your order.
　「服務生會過來請您點菜。」

*Here is the menu, sir.
　「這是菜單。」

*Could you call a waiter when you are ready to order?
　「如果您要點菜，請叫服務生。」

《單字和發音》

person	〔`p ɜ s n〕	(名)	人、人們
prefer	〔p r ɪ `f ɚ〕	(動)	~喜歡某樣
order	〔`ɔ r d ɚ〕	(名)	點菜、指示
immediately	〔ɪ `m i d ɪ ɪ t l ɪ〕	(副)	馬上、迅速的

1) How many persons, please?
2) How many persons are there in your party?
3) I'll show you to your table.
4) Your table is ready, sir.   Thank you for waiting.
This way, please.
5) I'm afraid that table is reserved, sir.
6) Would you like to wait at the bar until a table is available?
7) Would you mind sitting separately?
8) Will anyone be joining you later, sir?
(Is anyone joining you, sir?)
9) Shall I bring a high chair for your child?
10) I'll bring you the menu, immediately.

《置換練習》

1) Would you like a seat near the window?
close to the window?
by the window?
with a view of the city?

2) Could you wait a few minutes, please?
a little longer, please?
about five minutes, sir?

《請翻譯成英語》
1) *G*：請問有空位嗎？
   W：有的。請走這邊。
2) *G*：請問你有一人坐的桌子嗎？
   W：有的，先生。請問你希望坐在窗戶旁邊嗎？
   G：是的。
   W：請走這邊。
3) *W*：先生，晚安。請問你有訂位嗎？
   G：是的，兩個人。我是史密司。約翰・史密司。
   W：有的，先生。約翰・史密司先生。是兩位，請
   走這邊。
   G：好的。

[**Answers**]
1) *G*：Do you have a vacant seat?
   W：Yes, this way, please.
2) *G*：Do you have a table for one?
   W：Yes, sir.　Would you like to sit by the window?
   G：Yes, please.
   W：This way, please.
3) *W*：Good evening, sir.　Do you have a reservation?
   G：Yes, for two.　Smith, John Smith.
   W：Yes, sir.　Mr. John Smith, for two.　This way
   please.
   G：Sure.

Lesson 19 餐飲（接受點菜）

在餐廳接受點菜及點飲料時，英文是以 "take order" 來表示，此時服務的人員必須對客人的詢問，做充分的的說明。因此最好先了解料理的材料及烹調時間等的知識，才能夠從容的應付客人的問題。

Would you like to order now?

《 **Dialogue Drill** 》　　*G*: Guest, *W*: Waitress

W: May I take your order?

G: Yes, I'd like this one here. (points)　"Two Jumbo Eggs with Sausage".　And one order of English muffins as well.

W: Certainly, sir.　And how would you like your eggs ,sir?

G: Fried, please.

W: Sunny-side up or over easy?

G: Sunny-side up.

W: Would you like anything else, sir?

G: Yes.　I'd like a cup of coffee, please.

W: Would you like the coffee with the meal or after the meal?

G: After the meal would be fine.

W: Anything else, sir?

G: No, that's all.

W: Thank you, sir.　Just a moment, please.

您決定要點菜了嗎？

《會話練習》　　*G*:客人，　*W*: 女服務生

W: 請問要點餐了嗎？

G: 是的，我想要這個。
　　〝兩個蛋和香腸〞。
　　還要一份英式鬆餅。

W: 好的，先生。
　　請問先生您希望蛋要怎麼做？

G: 請用煎的。

W: 請問只煎一面或兩面都要煎呢？

G: 只要煎一面。

W: 先生，您還要點些其他的東西嗎？

G: 是的。我還要一杯咖啡。

W: 請問您的咖啡要用餐時一起用，還是要在餐
　　後呢？

G: 我要在餐後。

W: 先生，您還需要什麼呢？

G: 不用了，這樣就可以了。

W: 謝謝您，先生。請稍等一下。

《常用高頻率會話》
*May I take your order (now)?
 Are you ready to order (now)?
 Would you like to order (now)?
　「您要點菜了嗎？」

*How would you like your eggs?
　「您點的蛋要怎麼作？」
　　Fried egg 〔 sunny-side up: 單面荷包蛋
　　　　　　　　over easy: 兩面煎〕
　　Scrambled egg 〔炒蛋〕, omelet 〔煎蛋捲〕

*Would you like the coffee with the meal or after the meal?
　「您的咖啡要用餐時一起用，還是在餐後用呢？」

*Now or later?
　「現在，還是等一下？」
　這是省略前文的詢問方式，除了飲料、沙拉等，也可
　以用此種方式來詢問。

*Will there be anything else?
 Is there anything else?
 Would you like anything else?
「您還要點些其他的東西嗎？」

*You may have a choice of ~, ~, or ~.
　「您可從~中，選擇一個。」

*How would you like your steak?
「您的牛排要幾分熟？」
rare (3 分), medium (5 分), well-done (全熟)
可以上述的文句來表示。

*Excuse me.　May I take you plate, sir?
 May I clear the table?
 Are you through, sir?
「對不起，我可以把盤子收走嗎？」

*Would you care for some dessert, sir?
「先生，要不要來客甜點？」

*Would you like a separate check?
「您需要分開付帳嗎？（各付各的）」

*Could you pay at the cashier?
「請到出納付款」

*It is the Chef's Special.　(delight)
「這是主廚推薦的料理。」

*This dish can be prepared quickly.
「這些料理，很快就準備好。」

《單字和發音》
recommend 〔，rɛkə`mɛnd〕(動) 推薦
separate 〔`sɛpə，ret〕 (動) 分開

1) Here is the menu, sir. Please take your time.
2) I'll bring the menu right away.
3) Could you call a waiter when you are ready to order?
4) Have you decided, sir?
5) Would you like coffee or tea this morning?
6) I hope you enjoy your meal.
7) Please help yourself to the cream and sugar.
8) Please help yourself to a salad from the Salad Bar near the entrance.
9) It will take about twenty minutes to prepare it. Will that be all right?
10) May I remove your dish?

《置換練習》

1) How would you like your steak?
                        eggs?
                        bacon?

2) Would you like your coffee with or after your meal?
                 your tea with lemon or with cream?
                 a cocktail or some wine with your meal?

3) It is served with bread or rice.
                 a sweetened sauce.
                 a side dish of pickled vegetables.

《請翻譯成英語》
1) *G*: 請問吃 「sukiyaki」要配合什麼飲料才好呢？
   W: 我推薦您喝日本清酒，是一種米酒。
2) *W*: 您是否要從吧台點一些飲料？
   G: 是的。我想來一杯愛爾蘭咖啡。
3) *W*: 請問帳單要一起算還是分開來算呢？
   G: 請分開來算。
4) *G*: 我沒有時間，請問點什麼餐比較快呢？
   W: 如果點咖哩飯或是意大利麵會比較快。

〔 **Answers** 〕
1) *G*: What goes well with sukiyaki to drink?
   W: I recommend "Sake", a type of rice wine.
2) *W*: Would you like anything to drink from the bar?
   G: Yes, please.　I'd like to have an Irish Coffee.
3) *W*: Will this be all together, or shall I make out separate
      checks?
   G: Separate checks, please.
4) *G*: I don't have much time.　What can be prepared
      (served) quickly?
   W: Curry and rice or spaghetti can be served quickly.

Lesson 20 酒 吧 會 話

在酒吧的吧台，客人常常是一個人，如能在此時，多利用機會與客人談話，那麼你的會話能力也一定會大為進步。

We have lots of imported stuff, too.

《 **Dialogue Drill** 》　　*G*: Guest, *B*: Bartender

B:　Good evening, sir.

G:　Hello.

B:　Would you care for a drink?

G:　Well, give me a Scotch, please.

B:　What brand, sir?

G:　White Horse, double.

B:　Soda or water?

G:　Just plain water with plenty of ice.

B:　Have some potato chips, sir.

G:　Good!　Give me another one.　What is that bottle over there?
　　　(He points to a row of bottles.)
　　　Let me see it.
　　　(He is handed the bottle by the bartender.)
　　　You are pretty well stocked here.

B:　Yes, sir.　We have lots of imported stuff, too.

我們有不少外國進口的酒。

《會話練習》　　*G*: 客人，　*B*: 酒吧侍者

B: 先生，晚安。

G: 你好。

B: 請問您想要喝什麼飲料？

G: 請給我一杯威士忌。

B: 先生，要哪一種牌子呢？

G: 白馬牌，雙份的。

B: 要不要加蘇打水或是水呢？

G: 只要加水和多一點冰塊。

B: 先生，要來一些洋芋片嗎？

G: 好酒！再給我一杯。
　　那個瓶子是什麼酒？
　　(手指著一排的酒瓶。)
　　讓我看看。
　　(酒吧侍者把瓶子交給他。)
　　你進了不少好酒。

B: 是的，先生。我們有不少外國進口的酒。

《常用高頻率會話》

*What would you like to drink?
 What kind of drink would you like?
　「您要喝點什麼？」

*Which (what) brand would you prefer?
 Any particular brand, sir?
 What brand, sir?
　「您喜歡什麼樣的牌子？」

*Here is the beverage list.
　「這是飲料目錄。」

*Here is the appetizer list.
　「這是開胃菜單。」

*Would you like any appetizers with your drink?
 How about some appetizers, sir?
 Would you like to pick on something?
　「您要不要點份開胃菜來配酒？」

*We have imported and domestic beer.
　「我們有進口及國產的啤酒。」

*For your Martini, any particular brand of Gin?
　「您點的馬丁尼，要加什麼牌子的琴酒？」

*Would you care for another drink?
How about another drink?
Can I fix you another drink?
「您要不要續杯？」

*Excuse me, sir. It's closing time.
「對不起，先生。 到了打烊的時間。」

*The bar will be closing in half an hour.
「酒吧在 30 分鐘後打烊。」

*May I close (clear) your bill now?
「能否先結帳？」

《單字和發音》

whisky	〔 h w ɪ s k ɪ 〕	(名) 威士忌
brandy	〔 ˋ b r æ n d ɪ 〕	(名) 白蘭地
cocktail	〔 ˋ k a k ˌ t e l 〕	(名) 雞尾酒
wine	〔 w ɑ ɪ n 〕	(名) 葡萄酒
champagne	〔 ʃ æ m ˋ p e n 〕	(名) 香檳
dry	〔 d r ɑ ɪ 〕	(形) 較辛辣的 (形容酒)
sweet	〔 s w i t 〕	(形) 較甜的 (形容酒)
bitter	〔 ˋ b ɪ t ɚ 〕	(形) 較苦的 (形容酒)
appetizer	〔 ˋ æ p ə ˌ t ɑ ɪ z ɚ 〕	(名) 前菜、飯前酒、開胃菜
assorted	〔 ə ˋ s ɔ r t ɪ d 〕	(形) 拼盤
scotch and water	〔 ˋ s k ɑ tʃ ˌ ə n d ˋ w ɔ t ɚ 〕	威士忌加水
scotch and soda	〔 ˋ s k ɑ tʃ ˌ ə n d ˋ s o d ə 〕	威士忌加蘇打

《音調練習》

1) What would you like to drink?
2) What brand would you prefer?
3) Any particular brand, sir?
4) How about some appetizers, sir?
5) Here is the menu of the appetizers we offer.
6) Would you care for another drink?
7) How about another drink?
8) Can I fix you another drink?
9) We have imported and domestic beer.
10) We have lots of imported stuff, too.
11) Sign here and please put your room number, also.
12) May I close you bill now?

《置換練習》

1) How would you like your scotch?
                          martini?
                          bourbon?

2) Would you like to pick on something?
              any appetizers with your drink?
              another drink?
              to see the wine list?

134

《請翻譯成英語》

1) **B**: 先生，請問您的馬丁尼要怎麼調？
   G: 要完全不甜的。
2) **G**: 請問你有沒有清淡的食物可以下酒的？
   B: 要不要來一些什錦堅果、洋芋片、起司和脆餅或是意大利香腸。
3) **G**: 我想要喝土產的啤酒。你能建議我喝什麼呢？
   B: 先生，XXX 啤酒很受歡迎，你想不想喝喝看呢？
4) **B**: 您的波本酒要加水嗎？
   G: 是的。

〔 **Answers** 〕

1) **B**: How would you like your martini, sir?
   G: Make it extra dry.
2) **G**: Do you have anything light (simple) to pick on?
   B: How's about some mixed nuts, potato chips, cheese and crackers or sliced salami?
3) **G**: I'd like to try a local beer. What would you recommend?
   B: X X X beer is very popular, sir. Would you like to try it?
4) **B**: Would you like a wet-back with your (shot of) bourbon, sir?
   G: Yes, please.

Lesson 21　客房餐飲（ *Room Service* ）

　　客房餐飲(Room Service)用語，大部分的飯店
是指提供客房餐飲的服務，而與客房部的業務作一
個區別。因此， Room Service 大部分是屬於料理及
餐飲部門，因為客人常是經由電話來訂餐，因此電
話的應對是一個重點。

May I have your order, please?

《 Dialogue Drill 》　　　*G*: Guest, *O*: Order Taker

G:　Is this Room Service?

O:　Yes, sir.　May I help you?

G:　Yes.　I'd like to order the special steak dinner that
　　　is described in the menu in the stationery folder.

O:　Yes, sir.　How would you like your steak, sir?

G:　Rare, please.

O:　Would you like the baked potato or French fries,
　　　sir?

G:　I'd prefer the baked potato, please.　And I'd like
　　　coffee with my dinner.

O:　Is that all, sir?

G:　Yes, that will be fine.

O:　Thank you, sir.　I'll have your dinner sent up
　　　to you as soon as possible, sir.

G:　Thank you.　My room number is 310.

請點餐？

《會話練習》　　**G**: 客人，　**O**: 點餐服務員

G: 是客房服務部嗎？

O: 是的，先生。能為您服務嗎？

G: 是的。我想要點迎賓手冊裡的菜單上的特製牛排餐。

O: 是的，先生。請問您的牛排要幾分熟呢？

G: 要三分熟的。

O: 您要配烤馬鈴薯還是炸薯條呢，先生？

G: 我喜歡烤馬鈴薯，而且我還要一杯咖啡隨餐飲用。

O: 先生，這樣就可以了嗎？

G: 是的，這樣就夠了。

O: 謝謝您，先生。
我會儘快地把您的晚餐送去。

G: 謝謝你。我的房間號碼是 310。

《常用高頻率會話》

*May I have your order, please?
 Go ahead, please.
　「請點餐。」

*How many orders of coffee?
　「您咖啡要點幾份？」

*I'll repeat your order.
　「我重覆您點的東西。」

*At what time shall we serve it?
　「什麼時候給您拿去？」

*It should take about thirty minutes, sir.
　「大約需要三十分鐘，先生。」

*Your order should be there in about 20 minutes.
　「您點的東西，大約二十分鐘會給您送去。」

*May I have your room number, please?
　「請問您的房間號碼是幾號？」

*I'll have your dinner sent up to you as soon as possible,
 sir.
　「我會儘快將您的晚餐送過去，先生。」

*Could you leave the dishes on the tray outside your door?
「請您把餐盤放在您門外的托盤上好嗎？」

*Where shall I put the tray?
「您要我將餐盤放在那兒？」

*Could you sign the bill?
「請您簽一下帳單。」

*We have no tray service for cocktails.
「我們沒有提供雞尾酒的送房服務。」

*Our Tray Service includes club soda, Ginger ale, a bucket of ice, napkins, and a bottle opener.
「送房服務包括送蘇打水、薑汁水、冰塊、餐巾及開瓶器。」

《單字和發音》

bucket	〔`bʌkɪt〕	(名)	籃子、桶子
opener	〔`opənɚ〕	(名)	開罐器
tray	〔tre〕	(名)	托盤、盤子

《音調練習》

1) How many orders of coffee?
2) I'll repeat your order.
3) Room Service is offered from 6 a.m. to 12 midnight.
4) You will find the menu for Room Service in the stationery folder in your room.
5) How would you like your steak?
6) How many glasses will you be needing, sir?
7) It should take about thirty minutes, sir.
8) At what time would you like to have your breakfast served?   (sent up)
9) Shall I put it on your bill, sir?
10) Could you sign the bill?
11) Someone will be right there, sir.
12) I'll have it sent up to you as soon as possible, sir.

《置換練習》

1) May I have your room number, sir?
          have your order, sir?
          ask what time will be convenient, sir?

2) Where shall I put the tray?
                    wagon?
                    champagne?

《請翻譯成英語》
1) **G**: 請你送一些咖啡來好嗎？
   O: 是的，先生。請問要幾杯呢？
   G: 二杯。
   O: 好的，先生。我們立刻送去。
2) **G**: 我想要一杯 Cherry Blossom 。
   O: 對不起，先生。我們的客房餐飲服務沒有供應雞尾酒。
3) **G**: 這是 310 號房。我已經用餐完畢，希望你們把餐盤收走。
   O: 先生，我馬上派人去收。你只要把盤子放在門外就可以了。

〔 **Answers** 〕
1) **G**: Could you bring up some coffee, please?
   O: Yes, sir.　How many orders, please?
   G: Two, please.
   O: Certainly, sir.　We will bring it to you right away.
2) **G**: I'd like to have one Cherry Blossom.
   O: I'm sorry, sir, but we have no tray service for cocktails.
3) **G**: This is room 310.　I've finished eating and would like to have the dishes taken away.
   O: I'll send someone up right away, sir. Just leave the dishes on the tray outside your door.

附錄：飯店、餐飲常用單字

附錄：飯店・餐飲常用單字

設施　　　　　　§ PLACE

出納　　　　　　Cashier

櫃台　　　　　　Counter

住宿登記　　　　Register

公共電話　　　　Public Telephone

詢問處　　　　　Information

行李　　　　　　Baggage(美) / Luggage （英）

旅行箱　　　　　Suit Case

高爾夫袋　　　　Golf Bag

行李櫃台　　　　Bell Desk

職　稱　　　　　§ PERSONNEL

經理　　　　　　Manager

副理　　　　　　Assistant Manager

電話交換員　　　Operater

訂房　　　　　　Receptionist

出納	Cashier
行李員	Porter/ Bell Boy
電梯員	Elevator Operator
職員	Clerk
門僮	Door Man
男服務生	Waiter
女服務生	Waitress
料理師	Cook (Chef, Chief)
麵包師	Baker (Chief Baker)
各樓層的職員	Floor Clerk
洗碗員	Dish Washer
食品管理員	Pantry Man

職　稱　　　§ PERSONNEL

房務清潔人員	House Keeper
房務人員（男）	Chamber Boy
房務人員（女）	Chamber Maid

非洲人	African (Africa)
美國人	American (America)
阿拉伯人	Arabian (Arabia)
澳大利亞人	Australian (Australia)
奧地利人	Austrian (Austria)
英國人	British (England)
加拿大人	Canadian (Canada)
中國人	Chinese (China)
丹麥人	Dane (Denmark)
芬蘭人	Finnish (Finland)
法國人	French (France)
德國人	German (Germany)
希臘人	Greek (Greece)
印度人	Indian (India)

印尼人	Indonesian (Indonesia)
義大利人	Italian (Italy)
日本人	Japanese (Japan)
韓國人	Korean (Korea)
墨西哥人	Mexican (Mexico)
荷蘭人	Netherlander (Holland)
菲律賓人	Philippin (Philippine)
波蘭人	Polish (Poland)
葡萄牙人	Portugeese (Portugal)
羅馬尼亞人	Rumanian (Rumania)
俄羅斯人	Russian (Russia)
西班牙人	Spanish (Spain)
瑞士人	Swiss (Switzerland)
瑞典人	Swede (Sweden)
台灣人	Taiwanese (Taiwan)
泰國人	Thai (Thailand)

土耳其人	Turk (Turkey)

1. 飯店櫃台關係常用單字

單人房	Single Use
套房	Suit
白天用客房	Day Use
分配	Assign
預先分配客房	Pre-assignment
預先保留客房	Blocked Room
房間分配	Room Assignment
房間使用狀況表	Room Indicator
房間管理	Room Control
房間號碼條	Room Slip
房費	Room Charge
收費表	Tariff
換房間	Change Room
客房使用狀況表	Stock Card

住宿登記卡	Registration Card
交付記錄	Delivery Record
客人姓名管理架	Name Rack
隣室	Adjoining Room
旅行支票	Traveler's Check
預付金（存款）	Deposit
先付金	Advance
手續費	Commission
客人到達確認單	Arrival Slip
寄存給外部的（物品）	will call for
無事先預約的客人	Walk-in Guest
代理商	Agent
導遊	Tour Conductor
延長	Extension
額外費用	Extra Charge
超過預定的住宿	Overstay

重複登記	Double Booking
預約過多	Over Booking
房間使用率	Occupancy
收據	Voucher
接線生	Operator
留言	Message
館內電話	House Call
對方付費電話	Collect Call
叫號電話	Station To Station Call
叫人通話	Person To Person Call
掛號信	Registered Mail
郵局小包	Parcel Post
快遞‧限時	Special Delivery
接待室	Connecting Room
住宿附早餐	Continental Plan
確認	Confirm

免費招待　　　　　　Complimentary

帳單　　　　　　　　Bill

住宿優待券（付款後）　Hotel Order

住宿優待券（付款前）　Hotel Coupon

簽名　　　　　　　　Sign (Signature)

短距離送迎巴士　　　Shuttle Bus

貴重品　　　　　　　Valuable(s)

保險箱　　　　　　　Safety Deposit Box
（貴重品寄放箱）

親手交付與客人　　　By Hand Delivery

重要人物　　　　　　Very Important Person　（V I P）

會議　　　　　　　　Convention

轉寄用貼紙　　　　　Forwarding Slip

自動販賣機　　　　　Vending Machine

無效　　　　　　　　Void

遺失部品　　　　　　Lost and Found

不良客人　　　　　　Undersirable Guest

2. 餐飲常用基本單字

1. 料理的種類： §TYPES OF CUSINE

中華料理餐廳　　　　Chinese Resturant

北京料理　　　　Peiking　Cuisine
上海料理　　　　Shanghai Cuisine
湖南料理　　　　Hunan　　Cuisine
台灣料理　　　　Taiwan　　Cuisine
廣東料理　　　　Canton　Cuisine

西洋料理　　　　　　Western Cuisine

法國料理　　　　French Cuisine
義大利料理　　　Italian Cuisine
日本料理　　　　Japanese Resturant
韓國料理　　　　Korean Resturant

咖啡廳　　　　　Coffee Shop/ Bistro/ Cafeteria

餐廳　　　　　　Restaurant

簡餐　　　　　　Snack Bar

自助餐　　　　　Buffet

2. 餐　點　　§ Meal

早餐	Breakfast
午餐	Lunch
晚餐	Dinner/ supper

料　理　及　菜單　§ MENU

前菜	Appetizer
食前酒	Aperitif
湯	Soup
沙拉	Salad
調味醬	Dressing
主菜	Main Dish
肉類	Meat
飯類	Rice
麵包	Bread
套餐 (定食)	Fixed Price Menu
單點料理	Ala Carte (法語)

甜點	Dessert
飲料	§ TYPES OF BEVERAGE
飲料（無酒精 ）	Soft Drink
茶	Tea
日本茶	Green Tea
烏龍茶	Wou−Long Tea
紅茶	Black Tea
茉莉香片	Jasmine Tea
奶茶	Milk Tea
檸檬茶	Lemon Tea
水	Water
熱開水	Hot Water
冰開水	Ice Water
溫開水	Warm Water
礦泉水	Mineral Water
薑汁水	Ginger Ale

蘇打水	Soda Water
檸檬水	Lemonade
湯尼水	Tonic Water
果汁	Juice
可口可樂 （健怡）	Coke Cola (Diet)
可可亞	Cocoa

牛奶　　　　　　§MILK

鮮奶油	Fresh Cream
低脂牛乳	Low Fat Milk
脫脂牛乳	Skim Milk
全脂牛乳	Whole Fat Milk
奶粉	Powder Milk
優酪乳	Yogurt
罐裝牛乳	Canned Milk

咖 啡	§ COFFEE
黑咖啡	Black Coffee
卡布基諾咖啡	Cappuccino
無咖啡因咖啡	Decaffeined Coffee
濃縮咖啡	Espresso
普通咖啡	Regular Coffee
咖啡	Coffee
冰咖啡	Ice Coffee

酒 類	§ ALCOHOL
啤酒（瓶裝）	Beer （bottle)
啤酒（罐裝）	Canned Beer
生啤酒	Draft Beer
葡萄酒	Wine
紅葡萄酒	Red Wine
白葡萄酒	White Wine
粉紅葡萄酒	Rose Wine

香　檳	Champagne
雞尾酒	Cocktail
白蘭地酒	Brandy, Cognac
法國白蘭地	Cognac
琴酒	Gin
龍舌蘭酒	Tequila
威士忌（蘇格蘭）	Whiskey,　Scotch
波本威士忌	Bourbon
日本酒	Japanese sake
冷日本酒	Hiya Sake
熱日本酒	Atsu－kan
温日本酒	Nuru－kan
龍舌蘭酒	Daiquri
紹興酒	Shao Shing Wine
陳年紹興酒	V. O.　Shao Shing Wine

穀物	Allbran
麥片粥	Birchermuesli
藍莓甜點	Blueberry Muffins
奶油麵包	Brioches
泡牛奶穀片	Cereal
玉米片	Corn Flakes
法式牛角麵包	Croissants
丹麥麵包	Danish Pastries
英式麵包	English Muffins
法式麵包	French Bread
法式土司	French Toast
硬麵包卷	Hard Rolls
蜂蜜	Honey
英式圓麵包	Muffins

煎圓餅	Pancake
葡萄麵包	Raisin Muffins
黑麥麵包	Rye Bread
黑麥土司	Rye Toast (Brown Toast)
米花	Rice Crispies
軟卷麵包	Soft Rolls
糖漿	Syrup
華夫麵包	Waffle
大麥麵包	Wheat Toast
白土司	White Toast
全麥卷	Whole Wheat Rolls

蛋的料理法　　§ EGG

煮蛋（附殼）	Boiled Egg
蛋皮	Omelette
兩面煎蛋（半熟）	Over Easy
兩面煎蛋（全熟）	Over Hard

水煮蛋、帶殼	Boiled Egg
1. 較硬：	Hard—Boild Egg
2. 半熟：	Soft—Boild Egg
水煮蛋・無殼	Poached Egg
炒蛋	Scrambled Egg
單面荷包蛋	Sunny Side Up

水果類	§ FRUITS
西瓜	Watermelon
哈密瓜	Cantaloupe/ Muskmelon
木瓜	Papaya
蓮霧	Rose Apple
柳橙	Orange
柳丁	Navel Orange
葡萄柚	Grape Fruits
楊桃	Star Fruits
香蕉	Banana

蘋果	Apple
奇異果	Kiwi fruits
橘子	Orange
櫻桃	Cherry
百香果	Passion fruits
葡萄	Grape
芭樂	Grava
鳳梨	Pineapple
檸檬	Lemon
黃檸檬	Lime
草莓	Strawberry
酪梨	Avogado
梨	Pear
椰子	Coconut
枇杷	loguat (Pi−Pya)
芒果	Mongo

榴槤	Durian
荔枝	(Lai–Chi)
藍莓	Blue Berry
龍眼	(Long – Yen)
柿子	Persimmon
桃子	Peach
李子	Prum

甜點類 : § DESSERTS

蛋糕	Cake
甜餅	Pan cake
冰淇淋	Icecream
雪泥	Sherbet
鮮奶油	Cream Caramel
果凍	Jelly
慕斯	Mousse
派	Pie

磅餅	Pound Cake
布丁	Pudding
聖代	Sundae
水果餅	Tart

主食類 § FOOD

米飯	Rice
咖哩飯	Curry Rice
炒飯	Chao Fan, Pilaf
麵包	Bread
英國圓麵包	Muffin
麵類	Noodles
烏龍麵	Japanese Udon
日本麵（蕎麥）	Buckwheat Noodles
牛肉麵	Beef Noodles
湯麵	Chinese Noodles
餛飩麵	Chinese Dumpling

叉燒麵	Pork Noodles
炒麵	Fried Noodles
意大利麵	Spaghetti

沙拉調味料　　　§ SALAD DRESSING/BUTTER

藍起士	Blue Cheese
奶油	Butter
法式調味料	French Dressing
義大利調味料	Italian Dressing
人造奶油	Margarine
薄荷凍	Mint Jelly
菓實醋・油	Oil And Vinegar
千島醬	Thousand Island
醋油	Vinaigrette

佐　料	§ SAUCE
蕃茄醬	Ketchup/Tomato Sauce
辣油	Lea & Perrins/Worcestershire
鮮味醬油	Maggi Sauce
美奶滋	Mayonnaise
黃色芥末：美式	Mustard: American Style
黃色芥末：英國式	Mustard: English Style
黃色芥末：法國式	Dijon
醬油	Soy Sauce
塔巴司哥辣椒醬	Tabasco

調　味　料	§ CONDIMENTS
黑糖	Brown Sugar
低卡洛里糖	Low Cal/Equal
胡椒	Pepper
塩巴	Salt
糖	Sugar

166

醋	Vinegar

料理的材料

肉　類	§ MEAT
牛肉	Beef
沙朗（牛腰上部肉）	Sirloin
肋骨	Rib
菲利	Fillet
腿肉	Leg
牛舌	Tongue
牛尾	Tail
牛肉玉米醬	Corn Beef
豬肉	Pork
豬排	Pork Chop
火腿	Ham
培根	Bacon
肩肉	Fat Back

里肌	Loin
肝臟	Lever
腎臟	Kidneys

羊　　§ MUTTON-LAMB

山羊	Mutton
小羊肉	Lamp

雞　　§ CHICKEN

雞肉	Chicken
雞腿	Leg
雞翅膀	Wings
鴿子	Pigeon
火雞	Turkey
鵪鶉	Quail

鴨	§ DUCK
鴨	Duck
北京烤鴨	Peiking Duck
鵝	Goose

魚・海鮮類	§ SEAFOOD
魚	Fish
鮭魚	Salmon
鯉魚	Carp
比目魚	Brill
黃魚	Yellow Fish
魚子醬	Caviar
鮪魚	Tuna
鰻魚	Eel
鱈魚	Codfish
鯛魚	Seabream
鱸魚	Seabass

鰹魚	Bonito
鱒魚	Trout
香魚	Sweet Fish
鯖魚	Mackerel
鯡魚	Herring
沙丁魚	Sardine

蝦 · 其他　　§ OTHERS SEAFOOD

砂蝦 · 草蝦	Shirmp
班節蝦	Prawn
龍蝦	Lobster
蟹	Crab
鮑魚	Abalone
章魚	Octopus
花枝 . 烏賊	Squid
魷魚 （有骨）	Cuttlefish
干貝	Scallop

海參	Sea Cucumber
海蜇皮	Jelly Fish
魚翅	Shark Fin
文蛤	Clam
蚵仔	Oyster

其　他	§ OTHERS
蛙	Frog
鼈湯	Turtle (soup)
鹿	Venison
野猪	Wild Boar

青菜類	§ VEGETABLES
黄瓜	Cucumber
香菇	Black Mashroom
洋菇・草菇	Mashroom
葱	Scallion/Leek

洋葱	Onion
白菜	Chinese Cabbage
蘿蔔	Turnip
紅蘿蔔	Carrot
蕃茄	Tomato
馬鈴薯	Potato
甘薯	Sweet Potato
蓮藕	Lotus Root
芹菜	Celery
青椒	Pimiento/Bell Pepper
高麗菜	Cabbage
紫高麗菜	Red Cabbage
高麗菜球	Small Cabbage
竹筍	Bamboo Shoot
茭白筍	Water Bamboo Shoot
玉米	Corn

西洋萵苣	Lettuce
豆芽菜	Bean Sprout
茄子	Eggplant
南瓜	Pumpkin
冬瓜	Winter-melon
蘆筍	Asparagus
綠花椰菜	Cauliflower
花菜（白）	Broccoli
栗子	Chesnut

中國青菜　　§ CHINESE VEGETABLES

A菜	(A-Tsai) Chinese Vegetables
空心菜	(Konshin-Tsai) Chinese Vegetables
青江菜	(Chinkan-Tsai) Chinese Vegetables
菠菜	Spinash
茼蒿	(Ton-o Tsai) Chinese Vegetables
豆苗	Peas Vegetables

雪裏紅	(Snow–red) Chinese pickles
榨菜	(Za–Tsai)
紅豆	Red Beans
黃豆	Soy Beans
豌豆	Peas
絲瓜	Loofah
韭菜	Leek
苦瓜	Bitter Gourd
辣椒	Capsicum
黃芥末	Mustard
洋芥末	Horseradish
山葵	Wasabi
大蒜	Calic
生薑	Ginger
西洋香菜	Parsley
九層塔	Chinese Parsley

其　他	§ OTHERS
粉絲	Bean Flour Noodles
米粉	Rice Flour Noodles
通心粉	Macaroni
皮蛋	Million Egg
豆腐	(To－Fu) ， Bean Curd
蝦米	Dry Shrimp
海帶芽	Wakame
竹笙	Bamboo Sheet
燕窩	Swallow Nest
起士	Cheese
麥片	Oatmeal
早餐玉米片	Corn Flakes
果醬	Jam
牛油	Butter

調 理 法　　　　§ COOKING

盛裝	Assorted
烤	Baked
火烤	Barbecued
炒	Broiled
煮	Boiled
蒸	Steamed
炸	Fried
混合煮	Stewed

酒　吧　　　　§ BAR EQUIPMENT

吧湯匙	Bar Fork & Spoon
酒吧用刀	Bar Knife
果汁機	Blender
開瓶器	Bottle Opener
開罐器	Can Opener

調酒籤	Cherry Stick (Cocktail Stick)
拔軟木塞開酒器	Cork Screw
漏斗	Funnel
冰桶	Ice Bucket
冰杓	Ice Scoop
愛爾蘭咖啡酒精爐	Irish Cafe Burner
量杯	Jigger
壓檸檬機	Lemon Squeezer
紙杯盤	Paper Coaster
煙灰缸	Ashtray
雞尾酒調酒器	Shaker (Cocktail Shake)
酒瓶盤	Silver Bottle Coaster
吸管	Straw
冰酒桶	Wine Cooler (Champagne Bucket)
酒桶架	Wine Cooler Stand

玻璃製品	§ GLASSWARE
玻璃啤酒杯	Beer Glass
白蘭地杯	Brandy Glass
公杯	Carafe
香檳	Champagne Saucer
鬱金香檳杯	Champagne Tulip
紹興酒杯	Chinese Wine Glass
雞尾酒杯	Cocktail Glass
果汁杯（高林杯）	Collins
高球杯	High–Ball Glass
愛爾蘭咖啡杯	Irish Cafe Glass
烈酒杯	Liqueur Glass
馬丁尼酒杯	Martini Glass
波特酒杯	Port Wine Glass
雪莉酒杯	Sherry Glass
紅酒杯	Red Wine Glass

量杯	Shot Glass
夏天飲料杯	Siesta Hurricane
發泡酸酒杯	Sour Glass
水杯	Water Glass
威士忌酒杯	Whiskey Glass
白酒杯	White Wine Glass

杯子　　　　　§ CUP

湯碗（兩個把手）	Consomme Cup W/2 Handle
咖啡杯	Cafe Cup
中國茶杯	Chinese style tea cup
義大利濃縮咖啡杯	Demi–Tasse Cup
蛋架	Egg Cup
臘燭台	Glass Candle Cup
冰淇淋杯	Ice Cream Cup
茶杯	Tea Cup

壺類	§ POT & PITCHER
玻璃咖啡壺	Cafe King Decanter
咖啡壺	Coffee Pot
牛乳壺	Creamer
紹興酒壺	Chinese Wine Decanter
果汁壺	Juice Pitcher (Crystal)
黃芥末	Mustard Pot
醬油壺	Soy Sauce Pitcher
茶壺	Tea Pot
保溫咖啡壺	Thermos Cafe Pot
醋壺	Vinegar Pitcher
水壺	Water Pitcher
葡萄酒壺	Wine Decanter
刀	§ KNIFE
奶油刀・麵包刀	Knife (Butter and Bread Knife)
吧台刀	Bar Knife

蛋糕刀	Cake Knife
燒烤刀	Carving Knife & Fork
起士刀	Cheese Knife
甜點刀	Dessert Knife
晚餐用刀	Dinner Knife
切魚刀	Fish Knife
龍蝦鉗	Lobster Cracker
龍蝦刀	Lobster Knife
龍蝦夾	Lobster Pick
鮭魚刀	Salmon Knife
牛排刀	Steak Knife W/ wooden Handle

叉類　　　　§ FORK

吧叉	Bar Fork
雞尾酒叉子	Cocktail Fork
甜點叉	Dessert Fork
晚餐叉	Dinner Fork

魚叉	Fish Fork
牡蠣叉	Oyster Fork
服務叉	Serving Fork
蝸牛叉	Snail Fork
蝸牛夾	Snail Tongs
服務叉	Vegetabale Serving Fork

湯匙　　　　　§ SPOON

清湯匙	Bouillion Spoon
吧湯匙	Bar Spoon
咖啡湯匙	Cafe Spoon
魚子醬湯匙	Caviar Spoon
甜點湯匙	Dessert Spoon
義大利咖啡湯匙	Demi-Tasse Spoon
冰紅茶湯匙	Ice Tea Spoon (Long Spoon)
服務湯匙	Serving Spoon
銀製湯匙	Silver Spoon

湯匙	Soup Spoon
服務湯匙	Vegetable Serving Spoon

夾子‧杓子　　§ TONG ； LADLE

蛋糕鏟	Cake Spade
蛋糕夾	Cake Tong
冰杓	Ice Scoop
冰夾（塑膠把手）	Ice Tong W/Plastic Handle
服務瓢	Pastry Serving Tong
派鏟	Pie Server (Pastry Server)
沙拉鉗	Salad Tongs
肉汁長柄杓	Sauce Ladle
服務瓢	Serving Ladle
盛湯器	Soup Tureen
湯瓢	Soup Ladle
糖瓢	Sugar Ladle

盤子	§ PLATE
前菜用盤	Appetizer Plate
麵包・奶油用盤	Bread/Butter Plate
牡蠣盤	Clam & Oyster Plate
甜點盤	Dessert Plate
深湯盤	Deep Soup Plate
晚餐用盤	Dinner Plate
水果盤	Fruit Plate
玻璃圓形盤	Glass Round Plate
橢圓形盤	Oval Plate
橢圓水果盤	Oval Fruit Plate
甜點盤（水果派盤）	Pie Plate
盤蓋（有孔）	Plate Cover W/Hole
圓形盤	Round Plate
圓形深盤	Round Deep Plate
魚翅盤（附蓋）	Sharks Fin Casserol W/Cover

大皿	Show Plate
壽司用板	Sushi Plate
小盤	**§ DISH**
多用途醬碟	All Purpose Sauce Dish
奶油碟	Butter Dish
奶油盤（冰）	Butter Chilling Saucer
咖啡杯盤	Cafe Saucer
起士碟	Cheese Dish
法國清湯碗	Consomme Saucer
深碟子	Deep Dish
分菜碟	Divided Dish
義大咖啡用碟	Demi－Tasse Saucer
醬油碟	Soy Sauce Dish
毛巾碟子	Towel Dish

碗 類	§ BOWL
奶油碗（冰）	Butter Chilling Bowl
洗手碗	Finger Bowl W/Underliner
玻璃碗	Glass Bowl W/Cover
冰淇淋碗	Ice Cream Bowl
湯麵用碗（有蓋）	Noodle Soup Bowl W/Cover
核果用碗	Nut Bowl
洋葱用湯碗	Onion Soup Bowl W/Cover
餐盤蓋	Plate Cover
菓汁長杯	Punch Bowl
飯碗	Rice Bowl
奶酪碗（附皿盤）	Supreme Bowl W/Underliner
沙拉碗	Salad Bowl
魚翅用碗（有蓋）	Sharks Fin Bowl W/Cover
魚翅下墊用碗	Sharks Fin Bowl Underliner
小型玻璃碗	Small Glass Bowl

醬油碗	Sauce Bowl
湯碗	Soup Bowl
糖罐（附蓋）	Sugar Bowl W/Cover (or Lid)
魚子醬碗	Supreme Bowl

其他器具　　§ OTHER EQUIPMENTS

咖啡機	Coffee Machine
咖啡壺	Cafe Urn
咖啡保温器	Cafe Warmer
加熱器	Table Heater
鐵板燒	Teppanyaki
烤土司機	Toast Machine

其他　　§ OTHERS

小孩用椅子	Baby Chair
麵包用籃	Bread Basket (Oval)
蛋糕台	Cake Stand
蠟燭台	Candle Holder (Candle Stand)

砂鍋	Casserole W/Handle
筷子架	Chopstick Stand
木筷子	Chopstick Wooden
刀板	Cutting Board
碟子（附蓋）	Dish Stand W/Cover
花瓶	Flower Vase
水果台	Fruit Cake Stand
六角形麵包籃	Hexagon Bread Basket
果醬台	Jam Holder
肉叉	Meat Stick
哈密瓜用盤	Melon Soup Casserole
橢圓盤台	Oval Dish Stand
橢圓台	Oval Stand
橢圓保溫用蓋子	Oval Stand Cover
橢圓托盤	Oval Tray
叫人牌板	Paging Board

盤子蓋	Plate Cover
紅酒托籃	Red Wine Holder
預約席（名牌）	Reservation Sign
烤牛肉推車	Roast Beef Wagon
圓鍋	Round Casserrole
圓盤台	Round(Dish)Stand
塩巴瓶	Salt Mill
塩巴及胡椒瓶	Salt & Pepper Shaker
湯匙台	Spoon Stand
檯燈	Table Lamp
桌位號碼牌	Table No.　Stand
磨胡椒器	Tall Pepper Mill
銀製濾茶器	Tea Strainer(W/Wood Handle)
牙籤	Toothpick
毛巾籃	Towel Basket W/Tong

3. 房務常用基本單字

啤酒	Beer
杯墊	Coaster
可樂	Coke
水果	Fruit
玻璃杯	Glass
熱水	Hot Water
冰塊	Ice (Cube)
冰桶	Ice Bucket
果汁	Juice
刀	Knife
礦泉水	Mineral Water
七喜汽水	Seven-Up
蘇打水	Soda
湯尼水	Tonic Water

洗　衣　§ LAUNDRY

乾洗	Dry Cleaning
快洗	Express Service
洗衣	Laundry
洗衣袋	Laundry Bag
熨衣	Pressing

浴室關聯　§ BATHROOM

沐浴乳	Bath Foam
足巾	Bath Mat
浴袍	Bath Robe
浴巾	Bath Towel
浴缸	Bath Tub
按摩浴缸	Jacuzzi
乳液	Body Lotion
棉花球	Cotton Ball

置棉花箱	Cotton Box
棉棒	Cotton Tip
毛巾	Face Towel
水龍頭	Faucet
花	Flower
潤絲	Hair Conditioner
吹風機	Hair Dryer
手巾	Hand Towel
鏡子	Mirror
刮鬍刀	Razor
清潔袋	Sanitary Bag
洗髮精	Shampoo
淋浴帽	Shower Cap
淋浴噴水頭	Shower Head
淋浴間	Shower Room
肥皂	Soap

肥皂台	Soap Dish
洗面台	Sink
面紙盒	Tissue Box
面紙	Tissue Paper
馬桶	Toilet
衛生紙	Toilet Paper
牙刷	Tooth Brush
牙膏	Tooth Paste
變壓器	Transformer
體重器	Weighing Scale

寢 具　　　　§ BEDDING

床	Bed
床頭櫃	Bed Table
床單	Bed Sheet
被單	Bedspread
毛毯	Blanket
羽毛被	Duvet
被套	Duvet Cover
枕頭	Pillow
枕頭套	Pillow Case

文 具　　　　§ STATIONERY

聖經	Bible
飯店服務指南	Directory of Services
信封	Envelop
橡皮	Eraser
傳真用紙	Fax Form

火柴	Matches
雜誌	Magazine
便條紙	Memo
報紙	Newspaper
便條紙	Note Pad
筆	Pen
迴紋針	Paper Clip
名信片	Postcard
客房部餐飲菜單	Room Service Menu
針線包	Sewing Kit
訂書機	Stapler
訂書針	Staples
小刀	Utility Knife
信箋	Writting Paper
電話簿	Yellow Page

櫃 子　　　　　　　　§ CLOSET

櫃子	Closet
衣服刷	Clothes　Brush
衣架	Hanger
保險櫃	Safety Box
擦鞋紙	Shoeshine paper
鞋拔	Shoe Horn
購物袋	Shopping Bag
絲質衣架	Silk Hanger
吊裙架	Skirt Hanger
拖鞋	Slippers
雨傘	Umbrella

電氣用品　　　　§ ELECTRIC APPLIANCES

空調	Air Conditioner
鬧鐘	Alarm Clock
製冰機	Ice Maker

國際直撥電話	IDD　(International Direct Dialing)
冰箱	Refrigerator
換氣扇	Smoke Ventilator
立燈	Standing Lamp
暖爐	Stove
檯燈	Table Lamp
電話	Telephone
電視	Television
吸塵器	Vacuum Cleaner
錄影機	VCR (Video Cassette Recorder)

其他　　　　　§ OTHERS

樓層總鑰匙	Floor Master Key
骨董品	Antique
保母服務	Baby Sister
嬰兒床	Baby Crib (Baby Bed)
窗簾	Curtain

桌子	Desk
不要打擾	DND (Do Not Disturb)
門	Door
門鈴	Door Bell
電梯	Elevator (Lift)
安全門出口	Exit
滅火器	Fire Extinguisher
自動洒水裝置	Fire Sprinkler
行動不方便房間	Handicap Room
健身中心	Health Club
行李台	Luggage Rack
清掃房間	Make Up Room
按摩房	Massage Room
禁煙樓層	Non−Smoking Floor
貯蔵室	Pantry
房間鑰匙	Room Key

邊桌	Side Table
三溫暖房間	Sauna Room
煙霧探測器	Smoke Detector
吸煙層	Smoking Floor
沙發	Sofa
樓梯	Stair
游泳池	Swimming Pool
電視櫃	Television Armoire
夜床服務	Turn Down Service
廢物箱	Waste Basket
窗子	Window

健 康	§ HEALTH
感冒	Caught Cold
頭暈	Dizziness
挫傷	Sprain
打撲傷	Bruise
骨折	Fracture
受了傷	Injured
高血壓	High Blood Pressure
發燒	Feverish
牙痛	Toothache
胃痛	Have a stomachache.
心臟不好	Heart trouble
頭痛	Headache
割傷 擦傷	Cut
火傷	Burn

咳 嗽	Cough
藥	Medicine
阿 斯 匹 靈	Aspirin
眼 藥	Eyedrop
感 冒 藥	Cold Medicine
胃 腸 藥	Stomach Medicine
拉 肚 子	Diarrhea
醫 院	Hospital
救 護 車	Ambulance
醫 生	Doctor
感 覺 怎 樣 ？	How do you feel?
請 叫 醫 生 來	Please call doctor.
我 想 要 感 冒 藥	I want cold cure.
請 好 好 保 重	Take good care.

形 容 詞　　　§ ADJECTIVE

貴 的	Expensive

便宜	Cheap
好的	Good
壞的	Bad
大的	Big
小的	Small
熱的	Hot
冷的	Cold
鹹的	Salty
辣的	Hot
甜的	Sweet
厚的	Thick
薄的	Thin
明亮的	Light
暗的	Dark
長的	Long
短的	Short

硬的	Hard
軟的	Soft
有趣的	Funny
無趣的	Boresome
喧鬧的	Noisy
快的	Fast
遲的、慢的	Slow
流行招搖的	Loud
不鮮艷的 質素的	Dark

顏色　　　　　§ COLOR

黑色	Black
白色	White
紅色	Red
青藍色	Blue
綠色	Green

灰色	Gray
茶色	Brown
粉紅色	Pink

天氣・季節　§ WEATHER/ SEASON

春天	Spring
夏天	Summer
秋天	Autumn
冬天	Winter
梅雨季	Rainy Season
天氣	Weather
晴天	Sunny
陰天	Cloud
雨天	Rain
颱風	Typoon
季節	Season

日本姿與心：(日本系列1)

　　本書的內容詳盡地介紹日本地理、歷史、政治、經濟、企業經營、社會、教育、文化等，藉由本書讀者不僅能對日本這個國家有著初步的了解且能吸收日本的經驗以充實自己的國際觀。不論您是學生或是從事對日的經貿往來、教育工作者、赴日深造、甚至自助旅行 …，本書豐富的各種題材，會令人對日本的知識刮目相看。在日本已暢銷數十萬冊，並修訂增至 4 版，為介紹日本的經典名著。國內也承各大專院校列為教科書，佳評如潮。

作者：新日本製鐵能力開發室

價格： 300 元

日語中的關鍵語：(日本系列2)

　　本書以『 KEYWORD 』（關鍵語）的方式出發，並採用容易閱讀的中日文對譯之方式，使讀者提高學習的效率，並加快學習腳步。經由本書『關鍵語』的用法能正確地了解日本語及日本人的社會生活、及文化的面貌。內文中有「上班常用語句」、「季節問候用語」、「商業上用語」，字字珠璣，使您讀後不但可以了解各個關鍵用語的用法及時機，同時全書平假名注音可增加您閱讀的效率。

作者：石川島播磨重工・廣報部

價格： 250 元

日本鳥人：(日本系列3)

　　本書的作者為英美人士，他們以詼諧的手法及富想像力的插畫，描述日本社會與生活，並採『中、日、英』三國語言的對譯方式，讓讀者藉由不同語言的角度，來了解各個語言的表現。內容生動活潑，您可利用這些幽默的話題及字彙，增加說話的幽默感並增進人際關係。熟讀本書可以了解日本人的生活面，並增加字彙及表現能力。

作者： Tim Ernst ＆ Mike Marklew

價格： 180 元

日本人的秘密：(日本系列4：中、日、英對譯)

本書的作者以卓越的洞察力分析了日本人與外國人在思考與行動上的差異,簡潔並詳實地描述日本社會及日本人的思考模式。尤其是對日本人的消費行動,有精闢的分析。對欲揭開日本神密的面紗,一探日本企業與文化的面貌。同時本書作者是一位知名並促進日本國際化的文化人,我們相信:具有多元及柔軟的思考方式是學習語言之外必要條件。本書也以較中立的立場介紹了日本社會的現狀並強調了包容對方文化的重要性。本書並承蒙各大學教授、文化人士推薦。

作者：長谷川勝行

價格： 240 元

40 國語言習得法：(學習系列)

臺灣已逐漸邁向國際化,語言是不同文化之間溝通的橋樑,具備多國語言的能力,是在競爭社會中脫穎而出的必要條件。本書作者以現身說法提供學習語言的方法與經驗,並詳實地介紹各個語言的脈絡關係,可提高學習的效果,因而成為暢銷書。任何人都可藉由本書,擷取正確的學習方法,並增加自信,開創自己的將來。本書並特別推薦給學生及社會人士,了解如何藉由學習語言達到成功的人生,為一本勵志及學習外國語言前的必備方法書。

作者：新名美次

價格： 180 元

日本語習字帖：(日語系列)

此本習字帖製作的目的是針對國人開發,使學生先建立學習的概念,並將習字基礎打好,使學生在學習語言前,以先了解日語的構造及與中文的差異性,並附錄平假名、片假名習字帖、高頻率單字、日本人、中國人百家姓、數字的唸法等,以易於教師教授方式編排。並承各大專院校、高中職校、語言中心等踴躍訂購中。

作者：東漢日語文化中心

價格： 50 元

國家圖書館出版品預行編目資料

最新觀光飯店餐飲英語--初版--，台北市：
漢思發行：知遠總經銷，民85.
面；　　公分. --
譯自：Hotel and Restaurant English Made Easy
ISBN 957-99695-7-4　（平裝附卡帶）
ISBN 957-99695-8-2　（平裝）

1. 英國語言 – 讀本
　　805.18　　　　　　　　　　　85010894

" 最新觀光飯店　餐飲英語 "（附錄音帶）

中華民國 85 年 10 月 25 日初版 1 刷發行　　　　新台幣 350 元整
　　　　　　　　　　　　　　　　　　　（書 200 元錄音帶 150 元）

發行人：張　思　本
發行所：漢思有限公司
　　　　台北市敦化南路 2 段 1 號 7 樓
　　　　T E L：(02) 705-5848
　　　　F A X：(02) 702-0365
郵撥帳號：18418738
登記證：新聞局局版台業字第 6441 號

總經銷：知遠文化事業有限公司
地　　址：台北市木柵保儀路 115 號
電　　話：(02) 939-6007

版權所有・翻印必究